Raintree Steck-Vaughn

Illustrated
SCIENCE
ENCYCLOPEDIA

Volume
24

Projects

RSVP

**RAINTREE
Steck-Vaughn**

P U B L I S H E R S

The Steck-Vaughn Company

Austin, Texas

Published by Raintree Steck-Vaughn Publishers, an imprint of
Steck-Vaughn Company.

Executive Editor	Diane Sharpe
Senior Editor	Anne Souby
Design Manager	Joyce Spicer

This edition edited and designed by Andromeda Oxford Ltd.

Andromeda Editorial and Design

Project Manager	Julia Roles
Editorial Manager	Jenny Fry
Volume Editor	John Clark
Design	TT Designs, T&S Truscott
Cover Design	John Barker

Project Volume

Writer	Virginia "Crickett" Cassara
	Indian River County School System
Consultant	Sheryl Mercier
	Fresno Unified School District

Library of Congress Cataloging-in-Publication Data
Raintree Steck-Vaughn illustrated science encyclopedia.
        p.   cm.
    Includes bibliographical references and index.
    Summary: A twenty-four volume set containing brief articles
on science topics.
    ISBN 0-8172-3943-X (set)
    ISBN 0-8172-3942-1 (Volume 24)
    1. Science—Encyclopedias, Juvenile.   [1. Science—
Encyclopedias.]   I. Raintree Steck-Vaughn Publishers.
Q121.R354   1997
503—dc20   96-11078
                                  CIP
                                  AC

Printed and Bound in the United States of America.
1 2 3 4 5 6 7 8 9 10 IP 00 99 98 97 96

CONTENTS

INTRODUCTION

This book contains seventy-five projects that you can do to learn more about the fascinating world of science. Each project relates to one or more articles in the *Raintree Steck-Vaughn Illustrated Science Encyclopedia*. The titles of these articles are given in the **Research Connections** that follow the introduction to each project. If you use another encyclopedia or reference book, refer to the index. Some projects are experiments that allow you to perform tests to investigate scientific principles. Other projects include research activities that will help you learn more about a particular topic of interest. Many of the projects are suitable for science fairs and include suggestions about how you can share your project with your family, friends, and others. Science fair projects and the scientific method are explained in more detail on the next three pages.

Materials

Each project lists the materials you will need, in the order that you will need them. The projects have been designed to use materials that can be found in most homes. Occasionally you may need to buy an item. In addition to the materials listed, you will need paper and pencil or another writing instrument for most of the projects, so that you can record your observations and data (facts and information). You may want to keep a special notebook for your work on the projects. Collect all the materials you will need before starting each project.

Procedure

Each project is broken down into steps, so that you can easily understand and complete each one. Before you begin a project, read through all the steps so that you know exactly what you will be doing.

Safety is important whenever you do a science project. The projects include warnings to be very careful when using sharp objects, such as scissors. You should ask an adult's permission whenever you need to use a heat source, or ask an adult to help you. It is important to wash your hands after handling certain substances, such as soil, that could spread disease. Also dispose of these and any other such substances with care.

All of the projects require that you make observations. You need to take notes when you make your observations. Write down the date you make each observation, the time and location (if appropriate), and all the details you observe.

Making a chart or table will help you organize information about your project. A table has space arranged in rows and columns for the different kinds of data. Some of the projects contain sample tables. You can use these tables as models for creating your own tables for other projects.

Drawing Conclusions

This section of the project presents statements and questions that encourage you to draw conclusions from your recorded observations. You may want to go back and check an observation or repeat a part of the project to collect more data. Having drawn your own conclusion, you will have fulfilled the purpose of the project as stated at the end of the project's introduction.

Extension

Nearly every project description ends with a box labeled **Extension**. This shows you how you can expand the project by making additional observations. Some projects can be expanded for a science fair. If so, the extension box tells you how to do so. If a project has no extension box, it has a section called **Alternate Procedure**. This describes how you can use a different method to make observations to fulfill the purpose of the project.

SCIENCE FAIR PROJECTS AND THE SCIENTIFIC METHOD

In order to do a science fair project successfully, you need to follow a scientific method. There are many variations of this method, which scientists use as they experiment, and your teacher or school may have specific guidelines for you to follow. This section is meant to help you, but remember to check with your teacher about what is expected in addition to the guidelines that follow.

Selecting a Topic

When selecting a topic for your science fair project, be sure it is something on which you can perform experiments. Volcanoes may interest you, but you cannot do an experiment with an actual volcano, only with a model, and that may not be appropriate for a science fair project. Your topic should also not be too broad, such as "Plants." If you want to experiment with plants, narrow the experiment down to one specific aspect of plants, such as how they respond to light or to different materials as fertilizers.

Background Research

Once you have selected a topic, it is time to do research. Your teacher may or may not want a written report, but it is important to read about your topic to see what others have done with it. If a report is needed, take notes, list references (for a bibliography), and write your report after you have gathered enough information.

Statement of Purpose

You are now ready to come up with a one- or two-sentence statement of purpose, or problem. In other words, what are you trying to find out? If you state your problem as a question, your experimentation should lead to an answer to that question.

Model Project

In order to illustrate what is involved, Project 7, Freezing Points of Different Liquids, will be used as a model. Please refer to Project 7 as you read further.

In this case, your topic might first be "Liquids," but that is too broad. You need to narrow the focus to one property of liquids—freezing point—so as to have one specific thing to experiment with. Your research should include any information you can find about the freezing points of liquids. The problem (or purpose) could be stated as: "Do all liquids freeze at the same temperature?", or "Do different liquids have different freezing points?"

Making a Hypothesis

The next step in the scientific method is the hypothesis, or educated guess. Your hypothesis is a statement of what you think the outcome will be. (That is why you needed to do research first, so that you can make a logical statement of the hypothesis.) Your hypothesis might be: "Different liquids freeze at different temperatures" or "All liquids will freeze at the same temperature."

Listing Materials

The next step is to list all the materials that you will need. This list should be very specific, including measurements of sizes and quantities. For a science fair, your teacher may ask you to give such measurements in metric units. (In this volume, measurements are given both in customary units and in metric units.)

Identifying the Variables

In the next part of the scientific method, you identify the variables. This is necessary to make your experiment valid and scientific. The first variable is called the manipulated, or dependent, variable. This is the one thing in your experiment that you are deliberately changing in order to prove your hypothesis. In the example project, the manipulated variable is the different liquids that you are testing. You would state it in this way: "Manipulated Variable— Different liquids that are being tested."

The next variable is called the responding, or independent, variable. This is the change that occurs because of what you manipulated. In the example project, the responding variable is the freezing temperature of each liquid. In other words, you change the liquids, but the temperatures at which they freeze occur naturally. You would state this in your project in this way: "Responding Variable—Temperature at which each liquid freezes."

The controlled variables, also called constant variables, are everything you keep the same in order to make your experiment valid and scientific. In the example project, these include the size of the container used for both the liquid and the ice, the amount of ice and salt used, and the amount of each liquid. List these under "Controlled Variables."

Procedure

Procedure involves the steps you follow when carrying out your experiment. These steps should be written in such a way that another person can read them and then duplicate your experiment.

Recording the Data and Results

Throughout your project, keep a journal or log book to record every time you do anything dealing with experimentation. If you are growing plants, record every time you water or fertilize them. If your project involves measuring results over a period of time, record in your journal the time, date, and what you have measured or done.

While you are running your experiment, write down what occurred in an organized manner and present this information in a graph or chart. This information is called the data. In the example project, you would make a chart of the freezing temperatures of each liquid.

It is also important, in order to be scientific, to run your experiment three times, when possible, to obtain more accurate results. If you are doing a project such as growing plants under different colored lights, instead of doing the project three times you should have at least three plants in each group. All three trial results and an average should appear in your graph or chart.

Next, write your results. Use the data you have gathered to write several sentences summarizing your results. In the example project, the summary might be written as: "The liquids tested had different freezing temperatures, with only distilled water freezing at 32°F [0°C]. The other liquids tested took longer to freeze. The rubbing alcohol did not freeze."

Conclusion

The conclusion is the last part of the scientific method. In the conclusion, you answer your original problem question. You also need to state whether your hypothesis was correct. If it was not correct, do not go back and change it. Instead, write a revised hypothesis in the conclusion. In the example project, your conclusion might be: "Different liquids have different freezing temperatures. The hypothesis was correct." If your hypothesis was incorrect, the conclusion could be stated: "Different liquids freeze at different temperatures. The hypothesis was not proved. A revised hypothesis should state that different liquids do freeze at different temperatures."

Displaying Your Project

The sample project board shows one possible way to display all of the information explained above. The journal or log book may be displayed in front of your project at the science fair along with your report, if applicable. Again, be sure to consult your teacher or follow your school's guidelines.

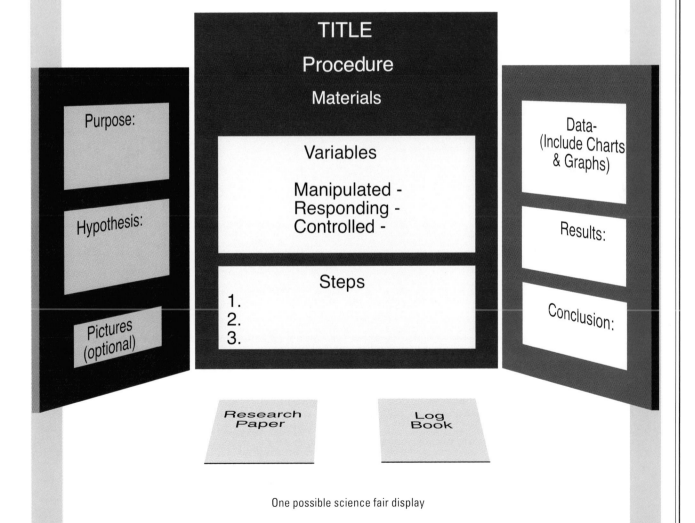

One possible science fair display

Acids and Bases

Acids are a group of chemicals with certain similar characteristics. All acids taste sour. When acids are dissolved in water, they release hydrogen ions (H^+). A chemist measures an acid's strength with a measurement known as pH (the potential for hydrogen). An acid's pH can range from 0 to 7. On the pH scale, 7 is neutral. On the other end of the pH scale is a group of compounds known as bases. Bases produce basic ions that combine with hydrogen ions. Bases have a pH range from greater than 7 to 14. When acids and bases are combined, they can become neutral. Strong acids (low pH) and strong bases (high pH) can burn flesh and are very dangerous.

One way to tell whether a substance is an acid or base is to use an indicator. An indicator is a substance that turns a certain color in the presence of an acid or base. The most commonly used indicator is litmus. In this project, you will make your own indicator from red cabbage and water.

Research Connections

ACID; ALKALI; BASE; INDICATOR; LITMUS; NEUTRALIZATION; pH

Materials

safety goggles
3–4 leaves of red cabbage (also called purple cabbage)
blender or food processor
water
measuring cup
strainer
10 small plastic cups
10 sticky labels
teaspoon
vinegar
ammonia
apple juice
baking soda
baking powder
detergent solution (a little powder or liquid mixed in a quarter cup of water)
lemon juice
milk
lemon-lime soda
shampoo solution (a few drops of shampoo mixed in a quarter cup of water)

soap solution (a small piece of soap shaken in a quarter cup of water)
club soda (carbonated water)

Procedure

CAUTION: Wear safety goggles when combining liquids.

1. Tear the 3 or 4 cabbage leaves into small pieces, and place them in a blender or food processor with 1 cup of water.
2. Blend well, then strain the mixture and use only the liquid.
3. Fill the ten plastic cups half full of water. Label them 1 to 10.
4. Add cabbage juice to each cup until each liquid is about the same shade of purple. This is your indicator.
5. To cup 1, add several teaspoons of vinegar. The solution will turn pink. This is your acid control. Any other solution that turns the indicator pink is an acid.

The acid control

6. To cup 2, add several teaspoons of ammonia. The solution will turn green. This is your base control. Any substance that turns the indicator green is a base.

The base control

7. Do not add anything to cup 3. This is your neutral control. Any substance that does not change your indicator's color is neutral.

The neutral control

8. Use cups 4–10 to experiment with other house-hold products, such as the ones listed in Materials above. Use only substances that are white, pale, or clear, because highly colored products will inter-fere with your results.

Use cups 4–10 to experiment.

Drawing Conclusions

Did the substances that gave an acid reaction have anything in common? Did the bases have anything in common? Only if you used products that can safely be tasted (consult an adult), touch a tiny bit of each with your finger and taste it. What taste did all the acids have in common? What taste did all the bases have in common?

Substance	Acid	Base	Neutral
Vinegar			
Ammonia			
Apple juice			
Baking soda			
Baking powder			
Detergent			
Lemon juice			
Milk			
Lemon-lime soda			
Shampoo			
Soap			
Club soda			

Record your results on a chart like the one shown above.

Substance with indicator	Effect of adding vinegar	Effect of adding ammonia

EXTENSION

You can expand this project for a science fair by forming hypotheses and doing experiments to answer the following questions: Can an acid mixed with a base actually neutralize a liquid? What ratios of acids and bases are needed to bring a cab-bage juice indicator back to neutral? A chart simi-lar to the one shown above can be used to record your results. For an explanation of the scientific method you will need to follow, see pages 5–7.

Air is a mixture of gases that surround the earth. Air is invisible, tasteless, and odorless. The force of gravity holds the air around the earth and gives it weight. At sea level, 1 cu. ft. of air weighs 0.081 lb. [1 cu. m weighs 0.130 kg]. When air is warmed, it expands, or takes up more space. When it is cooled, it contracts, or takes up less space. Thus, the temperature of air also affects its weight. When you look at an object that appears empty, it is actually full of air. In this project, you will show that air takes up space.

Research Connections

AIR; ATMOSPHERE; DENSITY; EXPANSION; WEIGHT

Experiment 1

Materials

1 crumpled tissue
1 clear plastic cup
1 tub or large container of water
1 small piece of polystyrene foam

Procedure

1. Place the crumpled tissue in the bottom of the cup.

Put crumpled tissue in the cup.

2. Turn the cup upside down, and push it straight down into the tub of water until it is completely underwater.

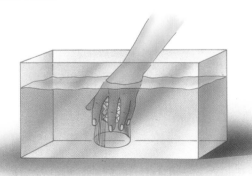

Push the cup underwater.

3. Lift the cup straight up out of the water. Remove the tissue from the cup and examine it.

Lift the cup out of the water.

4. Make a "boat" from the piece of polystyrene foam and float it on the water.
5. Put the cup over the boat and push it straight down.

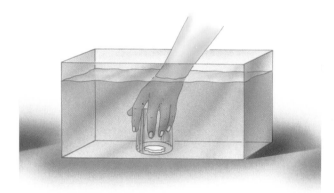

Push the cup over the boat.

6. Tilt the cup slightly underwater to let out a few bubbles of air.
7. Carefully pull the cup up to the water line, but not completely out of the water.

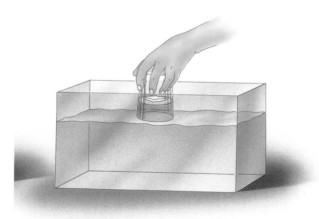

Pull the cup up to the water line.

Drawing Conclusions

Why do you think the water did not enter the cup when you pushed it underwater? How do you think the tissue stayed dry when it had been underwater (Step 3)? Why do you think there was water in the cup when you lifted it up to the water line (Step 7)?

Experiment 2

Materials

3 pieces of string, each 24 in. [60 cm] long
1 yardstick or meter stick
2 balloons of equal size
1 straight pin or safety pin

Procedure

1. Tie a string around the center of the stick.
2. Hang the stick up by the other end of the string.
3. Slide the stick on the string until it hangs balanced.
4. Blow up the two balloon and tie their ends.
5. Using the other two strings, tie the balloons to the ends of the stick. Adjust their positions until they hang balanced.
6. Use a straight pin or safety pin to pop one balloon. **CAUTION: Handle the pin carefully**. Observe what happens.

Drawing Conclusions

What happened to the balance of the stick when you popped one balloon? Why do you think this happened?

E X T E N S I O N

You can further investigate the property of air taking up space, and the expansion and contraction of warm and cold air, by tightly tying the ends of two balloons over the necks of two equal-sized bottles. Place one bottle in a bowl of very warm water and one in ice water. Observe what happens.

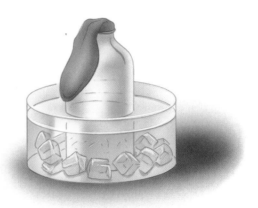

Attach balloons to the bottles and put into bowls of hot and cold water.

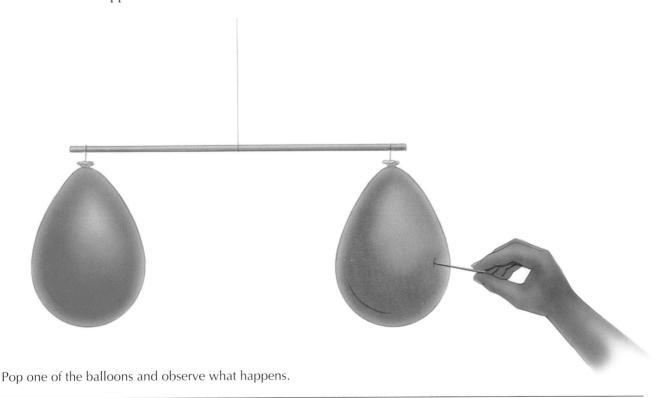

Pop one of the balloons and observe what happens.

Archimedes was an ancient Greek physicist, mathematician, and inventor. He discovered that when a solid object is immersed in a liquid, it is pushed up in the liquid by a force equal to the weight of the liquid it displaced. The weight of the liquid displaced is the same as the weight of the object. If the displaced water weighs more than the object, the object floats. If the displaced water weighs less than the object, the object sinks. When the object is immersed in the liquid, it weighs less than it does in air. In this project, you will investigate the displacement of water.

Research Connections

ARCHIMEDES; BUOYANCY; HYDROMETER; HYDROSTATICS; PLIMSOLL LINE

Materials

1 pencil (The six-sided type with flat edges works best.)
masking tape
1 12-in. [30-cm] ruler
2 identical plastic cups containing equal amounts of water

Procedure

1. Tape the pencil to the table to hold it steady.
2. Balance the ruler across the pencil.
3. Place a cup of water on each end of the ruler until it is again balanced.
4. Dip one finger into one of the cups. Be sure you do not touch the cup. Observe what happens to the water level in that cup.

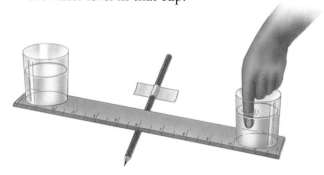

Dip in one finger and observe.

5. Observe the balance of the ruler.
6. Balance the two cups again. This time dip two fingers deeper into the water. Observe the water level and the balance of the ruler.

Drawing Conclusions

Why did the water level rise when you dipped your finger in? What happened to the balance and the water level as you dipped your fingers deeper into the water? Why do you think this happened?

EXTENSION

You can expand this project for a science fair by observing what happens when you place objects made of different materials in different liquids. Into a tall glass, carefully pour, one after the other, corn syrup, mineral oil, cooking oil, salt water (containing a little food coloring), and rubbing alcohol. Notice how the liquids settle in the glass.

Fill the glass with different liquids.

Carefully drop in small objects such as an eraser, a piece of wood, and a small plastic toy.

Immerse different objects.

Note where each object floats. For an explanation of the scientific method you will need to follow, see pages 5–7.

Buoyancy is what makes an object immersed in a fluid (liquid or gas) try to rise. In order for the object to rise, it must be less dense than the liquid (or gas) in which it is immersed. In this project, you will investigate raising and lowering the density of an object to make it float and sink. This is the same principle that a submarine uses to rise and fall in the water.

Research Connections
Buoyancy; Density; Fluid; Submarine

Materials
1 glass, cup, or jar, taller than the eyedropper
water
1 eyedropper (medicine dropper)
1 2-liter plastic soft drink bottle with a cap

Procedure
1. Fill the glass with water.
2. Partly fill the glass section of the eyedropper with water, and place it in the glass of water until it floats straight up and down. (Adjust the amount of water in the dropper until it does so.)

Fill the eyedropper so that it floats upright.

3. Completely fill the 2-liter bottle with water.
4. Place the eyedropper in the 2-liter bottle. (Do not squeeze the bulb to release the water you have in it or it will not float.)
5. Tighten the cap securely on the bottle.
6. Gently squeeze the sides of the bottle, applying more pressure until the dropper sinks.
7. Release and observe.

8. Repeat squeezing and releasing the bottle while you observe the water level in the eyedropper.

Squeeze the bottle.

Release the bottle.

Drawing Conclusions
Why do you think the eyedropper fell when you squeezed the sides of the bottle and rose when you released them? What happened to the water level in the dropper as you squeezed and released the bottle? What happened to the buoyancy of the dropper? Why do you think this occurred?

Alternate Procedure
An alternate procedure is to use a large-mouthed jar full of water. After placing the eyedropper in the water, cut the open end off a balloon and stretch the rest of the balloon over the opening. Secure it with a tight rubber band. Push down on the balloon and release.

Chromatography is a way of separating various dissolved substances in a mixture. Paper chromatography is based on the fact that porous paper absorbs various dissolved substances at different speeds and therefore, in a given time, to different extents. In this project, you will investigate paper chromatography as you separate substances from various mixtures.

Research Connections

Absorption and Adsorption; Capillary Action; Chemical Analysis; Chromatography; Separation; Solution and Solubility

Materials

several coffee filters or paper towels
scissors
several colored markers
several pencils or sticks
masking tape
water
several clear plastic cups

Procedure

1. Cut a coffee filter or paper towel into strips approximately 1.5 in. [35 mm] wide—one strip for each cup. Cut each strip about 1.5 in. [35 mm] shorter than the height of the cups. **CAUTION: Be careful when handling the scissors.**
2. Using the markers, make a large dot near one end of the strips (a different color on each strip) and allow the ink to dry.
3. Tape the other end of each strip to a pencil or stick.
4. Place about 2 in. [5 cm] of water in the bottom of each cup and lower the colored ends of the strips into the water. (The paper should barely touch the water. Adjust the water level if necessary.) The colored dots must not be allowed to touch the water.
5. Set the pencils or sticks across the rims of the cups to hold up the strips of paper.

6. Allow the strips to remain in place for about an hour. Observe the movement of the colors up the strips.

Leave the strips for about an hour.

Drawing Conclusions

Where did the bands of color come from? Why do you think the colors rose to different levels on the paper strips?

E X T E N S I O N

You can expand this project for a science fair by using other liquids (such as nail polish remover or rubbing alcohol) and comparing the results. **CAUTION: The fumes from nail polish remover are dangerous.** You can also try using different types of pens to make the colored dots. For an explanation of the scientific method you will need to follow, see pages 5–7.

Combustion, or burning, is a chemical reaction that gives off heat and light. Oxygen (usually in the air), fuel, and heat are all needed for combustion to take place. If one of these is removed, the burning stops. In this project, you will investigate what happens to a fire when its available oxygen is used up.

Research Connections

CARBON DIOXIDE; COMBUSTION; FIRE PROTECTION; OXYGEN

Materials

1 candle (in a holder)

matches

1 clear glass jar taller than the candle and wider than the base of the candle holder

Procedure

CAUTION: Fire is dangerous. Do this project only in the presence of an adult.

1. Light the candle and allow it to burn for several seconds.
2. Turn the jar upside down and carefully lower it over the candle.
3. Observe what happens.

Carefully lower the jar over the candle.

Drawing Conclusions

What happened to the candle flame? Why do you think this occurred? What happened to the oxygen in the jar?

EXTENSION

You can further investigate the property of combustion by placing the candle in its holder at one end of an empty aquarium (see illustration below). Sprinkle baking soda (bicarbonate of soda) over the base of the aquarium, and light the candle. Pour half a cup [0.2 liter] of vinegar into one corner of the aquarium and watch what happens to the candle as oxygen (air) is forced out of the aquarium by the carbon dioxide gas produced.

Pour vinegar onto the baking soda.

Freezing Points of Different Liquids

The temperature at which a liquid turns into a solid is called its freezing point. Different liquids have different freezing points. Also, dissolving a substance in a liquid affects its freezing point, making it lower. In this project, you will investigate the freezing points of several liquids.

Research Connections

FREEZING AND FREEZING POINT; LIQUID; SOLUTION AND SOLUBILITY

Materials

1 marking pen
1 tall, narrow glass container (An olive jar or baby bottle is ideal.)
1 plastic bowl, can, or other container, two to three times wider than the glass container
1 thermometer
ice
salt
several test liquids, such as milk, salt water, rubbing alcohol, vinegar, and water
record sheet

Procedure

1. Draw a mark on the glass container to indicate filling level (about one-half to three-quarters full).
2. Fill to the mark with one test liquid.

Pour in test liquid up to the mark.

3. Set the glass container in the bowl or can.
4. Insert the thermometer vertically into the test liquid.
5. Fill the bowl or can with ice.
6. Pour salt on the ice. Be careful not to get it in your test liquid.

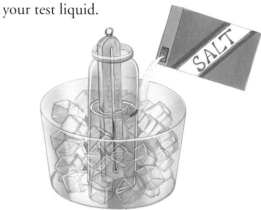

Pour salt onto the ice.

7. Place the experiment in the freezer. Check it at three- to five-minute intervals, removing it as soon as it appears to begin freezing. Record its temperature.
8. Rinse the glass and dry it.
9. Repeat Steps 2 through 8 with several other test liquids. You may use the same container of ice and salt each time, adding more as needed.

Drawing Conclusions

Did each liquid freeze at the same temperature, or at a different temperature? Did any of the liquids you tested freeze at the point usually considered "freezing" (32°F [0°C]—the freezing point of pure water)? How would you explain the reasons for the differences? Were there any test liquids that did not freeze?

E X T E N S I O N

You can expand this project for a science fair by first predicting the freezing point of each liquid and then testing your hypothesis. You could also test different concentrations of salt solution and measure their freezing points. Is there a relationship between concentration and freezing point? For an explanation of the scientific method you will need to follow, see pages 5–7.

Making Crystals

A crystal is a solid with a definite geometric shape. The shape consists of smooth, flat surfaces that meet in sharp edges or corners. Salt and sugar are examples of two substances that have crystal shapes. In this project, you will investigate growing several types of crystals.

Research Connections

CRYSTAL; SODIUM CHLORIDE; SOLUTION AND SOLUBILITY

Materials

2 clear plastic cups, one containing very warm tap water

salt or potassium aluminum sulfate (also called alum; it can be purchased at a drugstore or food store in the spice section)

1 piece of cotton string, twice as long as the height of the cup

1 paper clip

1 pencil

magnifying glass

Procedure

1. Pour salt (or potassium aluminum sulfate) into the cup of warm water and stir until it is dissolved.
2. Keep adding a little more at a time and stir until no more will dissolve.
3. Pour this solution into the other cup.
4. Tie a paper clip to one end of the string and lower it into the solution.
5. Tie the other end of the string around the pencil and lay it across the rim of the cup.
6. Keep the cup still (undisturbed) and check the string daily for several weeks.

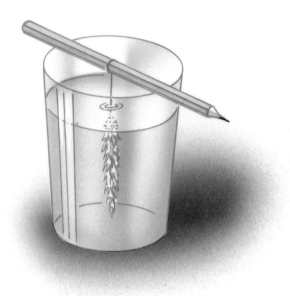

Check the string for several weeks.

Drawing Conclusions

How would you describe the material that forms on your string? Use a magnifying glass and observe your crystals.

Dissolve salt or alum in warm water.

EXTENSION

You can expand this project for a science fair by setting up several glasses with different dissolved substances (for example, table salt, Epsom salts, and sugar) or by selecting one substance to dissolve in water at different temperatures and comparing the results. How do substances and temperature affect the size of crystals? For an explanation of the scientific method you will need to follow, see pages 5–7.

Distillation is a process that separates a mixture into the liquids or solids of which it is made. Distillation usually involves the change of a substance into a vapor that is then condensed to its liquid form. In this project you will investigate ways to extract (distill) water from different mixtures.

Research Connections

DISTILLATION; EVAPORATION; SEPARATION; WATER SUPPLY

Materials

1 large pan or tub

salt

sand

water

1 glass or cup, shorter than the pan

2 small, clean rocks (scrub them if necessary)

1 large piece of clear plastic, large enough to cover the top of the pan or tub

masking tape

Procedure

1. Set the pan in a sunny spot outdoors.
2. Mix half a cup of salt and half a cup of sand with enough water to fill the pan about 2 in. [5 cm] deep.
3. Place the glass in the center of the pan and place a rock in the glass to weigh it down enough to stand in the water.
4. Cover the pan with the plastic. Pull the plastic tightly and tape it to the pan.
5. Place the other rock in the center of the plastic, directly over the glass. This will make an indentation in the plastic over the glass. Do not allow the plastic to touch the glass.
6. Wait several hours and check the glass. If no water has collected, allow more time, or add another rock to the center of the plastic to increase the indentation over the glass.

Drawing Conclusions

Once water has collected in the glass, remove the glass from the pan, hold it up, and look at it. Does the water appear clear? Taste just a drop. Is it salty? Why or why not?

Alternate Procedure

An alternate procedure is to use black plastic instead of clear plastic to cover the pan. With black plastic, does water collect in the glass faster or slower than with clear plastic? Why do you think this is so?

The completed distillation set-up using black plastic

Carbonated drinks, such as sodas, contain bubbles that give them fizz. The bubbles are carbon dioxide gas that is dissolved in the soda under pressure. You may have noticed that when you put ice or a straw into carbonated drinks, the bubbles tend to cling to the ice or straw. You also may have noticed that as the bubbles rise to the surface, they break. In this project, you will make your own carbonated liquid to make solid objects float and sink.
(**CAUTION: Do not drink it!**)

Research Connections
BUOYANCY; CARBON DIOXIDE; EFFERVESCENCE; GAS

Materials
1 large clear glass or jar (tall and narrow works best)
2 cups [0.5 liter] of water
baking soda
materials such as raisins, round candies, or uncooked spaghetti broken into 1-in. [2.5-cm] pieces
vinegar

Procedure
1. Pour 2 cups [0.5 liter] of water into the glass.
2. Add 2 tablespoons of baking soda and stir until it is dissolved.
3. Drop in several raisins, round candies, or spaghetti pieces.
4. Add 3 tablespoons of vinegar and observe for several minutes. If no action occurs except bubbling, add another tablespoon each of baking soda and vinegar.
5. As the action in the glass slows down, add more vinegar.

Drawing Conclusions
What caused the fizzing action in the glass? Why did the objects rise? What made them fall again? If you are not sure, observe again. Watch the objects (and the bubbles) on the bottom, then observe them at the surface.

Watch the objects rise and fall.

EXTENSION

You can expand this project for a science fair by first making a hypothesis of which objects will float the longest and sink the fastest. Good objects to try for this would be peeled and unpeeled grapes. You can also try liquids other than water, such as cola or club soda. If you use the baking soda, vinegar, and water combination, find out which ratio of the three makes the grapes rise and fall for the longest time. For an explanation of the scientific method you will need to follow, see pages 5–7.

Water freezes into solid ice at 32°F [0°C]. When another substance, such as salt, is added to the water before or after it freezes, the freezing point is lowered. In other words, a temperature lower than 32°F [0°C] must be reached for salt water to freeze or for a mixture of ice and salt to remain frozen. This is why salt is scattered on ice to make it melt. The salt solution has a lower freezing temperature than pure water, so the ice begins to melt. However, as the ice melts and dilutes the salt solution, it may again begin to freeze. In this project, you will investigate this phenomenon.

Research Connections
Freezing and Freezing Point; Ice; Water

Materials
1 glass of cold water
1 ice cube
salt
a piece of string

Procedure
1. Place the ice cube in the glass of water.
2. Try to lift the ice cube from the water with the string.
3. Lay the string over the top center of the ice cube and sprinkle salt on the string and the ice cube.
4. Count to ten, then slowly lift.
5. Or, place the ice cube on a table, lay the string across the top, and sprinkle on salt. Observe what happens.

Drawing Conclusions
Using what you learned in the introduction, explain why you were able to lift the ice after the salt was added but not before.

Sprinkle salt on the floating ice.

Sprinkle salt on the string.

EXTENSION

You can investigate this project further by trying substances other than salt, such as sugar, baking soda, or baking powder, to lower the freezing point of ice.

Expansion of Ice

Ice is the frozen form of water. When water is cooled, it contracts until its temperature drops to 39°F [4°C]. It then expands until the temperature drops to 32°F [0°C], the freezing point of water. Because it expands, ice is less dense than liquid water. That is why ice cubes and icebergs float. In this project, you will investigate the expansion of water below 39°F [4°C].

Research Connections

DENSITY; FREEZING AND FREEZING POINT; ICE; ICEBERG

Materials

2 identical thick glasses or jars
water
kitchen, postage, or balance scale

Procedure

1. Place equal amounts of water in each of the jars or glasses. Use a kitchen, postage, or balance scale to make sure they are the same.

Fill two thick glasses to the same level.

2. Put one glass in the freezer and leave the other at room temperature.
3. After several hours, weigh them again.
4. If a scale is not available, fill each jar or glass about three-quarters full.
5. Compare the levels after one has been frozen.

Drawing Conclusions

Did the ice weigh the same as the water? Why did the ice take up more space than the water?

E X T E N S I O N

You can investigate this project further by making your own iceberg. Fill a plastic bag three-quarters full with water, seal the bag, and place it in the freezer for several hours. Take the ice out of the bag and float it in a container of water. Estimate how much of your iceberg is above water and how much is below.

Make a lump of ice by freezing a bag of water.

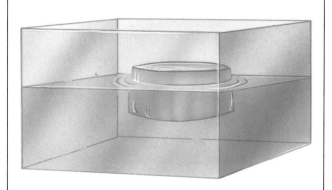

Float the ice in a tank of water.

The factory or plant that manufactures a product has to be sure that, when the product reaches a store or other retail outlet, it is not damaged. For this reason, manufacturers have to be very careful how they package their goods. To package them, they use materials called insulation. These materials protect the product against physical damage. Most people know these materials as packaging. In this project, you will test the best way to package one of the most fragile of objects—an egg.

Research Connections

IMPACT; INSULATION; SHOCK

Materials

materials that insulate against impact, such as shredded newspaper, polystyrene foam packing pieces, plastic foam packing, popcorn, or other material that could protect a product from impact

1 shoebox

several raw eggs

masking tape, string, or two large rubber bands

a stepladder or other safe elevated place to stand

Procedure

1. Fill the shoebox halfway with packing material.
2. Position one raw egg in the center of the packing material.

Place an egg in the center of the box.

3. Fill the remainder of the box with the packing material.

Fill the box with packing material.

4. Put the lid on the box and tape it or tie it shut, or use the two large rubber bands to keep it closed.
5. Stand in a safe elevated spot and drop the box. (Do not throw it, just drop it.)

Drop the box.

6. Open the box and check the egg. If it survived the fall, use it again and try other insulating materials. If not, clean out the box, get another egg, and repeat several times using several different kinds of packing material.
7. If no egg survived unbroken, try a lower elevation.

Drawing Conclusions

What packing material worked best? Which did not work? How might your results be different if you used a larger box with more insulation? What do you think would happen if you combined several materials in one box? Try doing this.

E X T E N S I O N

You can expand this project for a science fair by selecting different kinds of packaging material and dropping them from the same height. (It would be best to use the same weight of each material.) Try to predict which type of packaging provides the best protection. You can then test the best packing material when it is dropped from different heights. For an explanation of the scientific method you will need to follow, see pages 5–7.

The movement of a liquid through a semipermeable membrane from one solution to another is called osmosis. A semipermeable membrane is a thin piece of material that allows only a part of a mixture of dissolved substances to pass through it. The amount depends on the size of the molecules of the substance and their concentrations on each side of the membrane. Usually, substances that have big molecules have trouble passing through a semipermeable membrane. Small molecules usually have no problem. If there are two solutions on each side of a semipermeable membrane, liquids from the weaker solution will pass through the membrane more easily and mix with the stronger solution. In this project, you will investigate the way in which substances cross membranes.

Research Connections

MEMBRANE; OSMOSIS; SOLUTION AND SOLUBILITY

Materials

1 teaspoon
half a raw white potato
1 small bowl or dish
water
food coloring
1 permanent black marker
sugar

Procedure

1. Use the teaspoon to scoop out a large hollow in the center of the potato half.

Scoop a hollow in a potato.

2. Fill half the bowl with water, and put several drops of food coloring into the water.
3. Set the potato, skin-side down, in the water. If it does not float, add more water.

Float the potato in water.

4. Use the marker to draw a line on the potato's skin to indicate the water level at that time.
5. Place several teaspoons of sugar in the hollow in the potato.

Add sugar to the hollow of the potato.

6. Leave the experiment set up for several hours. Observe the change in the water level outside the potato. Mark the new level on the potato skin with the permanent marker.

Drawing Conclusions

What happened in the hole of the potato? Where did the water come from (is it colored)? What happened to the level of the water outside after the potato had been in it for several hours? Using the information in the introduction, can you explain why the water level changed?

EXTENSION

You can expand this project for a science fair by using variables such as different amounts of sugar, different water temperatures, or different kinds or sizes of potatoes. For example, take two identical potato halves and scoop out identical holes in them. Set one in a bowl of hot water and the other in a bowl of cold water. How does the temperature of the water affect the rate of osmosis in the potatoes? For an explanation of the scientific method you will need to follow, see pages 5–7.

A physical change is any change that happens to a substance without affecting its chemical composition. That is, its physical appearance may change, including its size, shape, or state (solid, liquid, or gas). For example, steam, water, and ice are three states of a liquid, but regardless of the state, it is still water. In this project, you will make a delicious physical change.

Research Connections
LIQUID; PHYSICAL CHANGE; SOLID; STATES OF MATTER

Materials
1 cup [0.25 liter] of milk
1/4 teaspoon of vanilla
1 teaspoon of sugar
1 1-pint [0.5-liter] zip-up plastic bag
1 1-gallon [3.7-liter] zip-up plastic bag
ice
1/4 cup [0.06 liter] of salt

Procedure
1. Mix the milk, vanilla, and sugar in the pint zip-up plastic bag. Be sure it is sealed tightly.

Mix the ingredients in the plastic bag.

2. Fill the gallon bag with ice and salt.
3. Place the pint bag in the gallon bag.

Place the small bag with the mixture in a large bag of ice and salt.

4. Zip the gallon bag securely.
5. Shake the bag gently or pass it from one hand to the other for about five minutes.
6. Open the gallon bag and observe the mixture in the pint bag. If it is not solid, reclose the bags and shake again. Continue until the milk mixture is solid.
7. Remove the pint bag from the gallon bag, wipe it clean of the salt-ice mixture, open, and eat!

Drawing Conclusions
Describe the physical changes you observed. What happened to the sugar (a solid)? What caused the liquid (milk) to change to a solid (ice cream)? Although it physically looks different, is your ice cream still just milk, vanilla, and sugar mixed together and frozen?

Alternate Procedure
An alternate procedure is to put a liquid freezer pop (the type that comes from the grocery store enclosed in a plastic strip) in the gallon bag of ice and salt. Shake and observe the physical change.

A chemical change happens when elements and compounds react together to form different compounds. A chemical change differs from a physical change in that the chemical composition is changed in a chemical change. That is, a new substance is formed. Typically in a chemical change, a solid is formed, a gas is given off, heat is produced, or light is produced. However, in a chemical change, physical changes may also occur. In this project, you will investigate the heat change (either heat produced or heat lost) and the formation of a new substance in a chemical change.

Research Connections

COMPOUND; ELEMENT; ENDOTHERMIC REACTION; EXOTHERMIC REACTION

Materials

safety goggles
1 1-gallon [3.7-liter] zip-up plastic bag
$^1/_4$ cup [0.06 liter] of vinegar
1 small pill bottle or medicine cup
baking soda (enough to fill the bottle
  or medicine cup)
thermometer
record sheet

Procedure

CAUTION: Wear safety goggles when handling any chemicals. Do not get vinegar in eyes.
1. Pour the vinegar into the plastic bag.
2. Fill the bottle or cup with baking soda.
3. Carefully set the container with the baking soda into the bag.

Set the container of baking soda into the bag of vinegar.

4. Hold onto the bag by yourself if you can; otherwise, get someone to help you with the next two steps.
5. Place the thermometer in the vinegar and record the temperature.
6. Zip the bag shut securely.
7. Let go of the container of baking soda to allow it to spill into the vinegar. Observe what happens.
8. Record the temperature of the vinegar again.

Drawing Conclusions

What change did you observe in the bag as the vinegar and baking soda mixed? Could you see a new substance fill the bag? What do you think it was? Was heat given off? How do you know?

EXTENSION

You can investigate this chemical change further by making a rocket fueled by the carbon dioxide gas given off as a result of mixing vinegar and baking soda. **CAUTION: Do this outside in the presence of an adult.** You will need a bottle with a tight-fitting cork. Place one-half cup of water and one-half cup of vinegar in the bottle. Place 1 teaspoon of baking soda in a paper towel, roll it up, and twist the ends. Drop the paper towel into the bottle and quickly put the cork in securely. (**Make sure the bottle is not pointing toward anyone!**) As the liquid soaks through the paper towel, the chemical change will take place. You may want to decorate the bottom of the cork with lengths of ribbon or paper streamers before "launching your rocket."

Saltwater Intrusion

Saltwater intrusion occurs when salt water intrudes, or enters, a supply of fresh water. This usually occurs in coastal communities where ocean water seeps into freshwater aquifers. Aquifers are important underground water reservoirs. In many places, people get water from wells that have been drilled into aquifers. When too much fresh water is taken from an aquifer, salt water may intrude or enter the freshwater zone. Living things are affected by the salt water: they become dehydrated and die. In this project, you will experiment with the effects of salt water on some living tissues.

Research Connections

AQUIFER; OSMOSIS; WATER SUPPLY; WELL

Materials

knife or potato peeler
French-fry cutter (optional)
1 raw white potato
2 plastic cups
water
salt
2 sticky labels
1 ruler
1 balance scale (if available)
record sheet

Procedure

CAUTION: Handle the knife and cutter carefully. You may ask an adult for help.

1. Carefully peel the potato. Cut strips from the potato about 0.5 in. by 0.5 in. by 2 in. [1 cm by 1 cm by 5 cm]. A French-fry cutter works great. Choose two strips that are as close in size as possible.

Peel the potato (above)
and slice it (right).

Choose two potato strips of the same size.

2. Fill each cup about three-quarters full with water.
3. To one cup, add one tablespoon of salt. Stir to dissolve the salt.
4. Label the cups "fresh" and "salt."
5. Make a table and record each potato's color, texture, length, and, if possible, weight.
6. Place one potato strip in each cup and let them stand for at least an hour.

Label the cups and put a potato strip in each.

7. Remove both potato strips and again record their color, texture, length, and weight. Compare these observations with the first ones.

Drawing Conclusions

How were the potato strips different after they had been left to stand in the water? Which one had the greatest change? Why do you think so?

EXTENSION

You can expand this project for a science fair by observing salt water's effect on other vegetables and fruits, as well as on slices of raw meat. **Always wash your hands after handling raw meat.** Be sure to formulate your hypothesis before testing. For an explanation of the scientific method you will need to follow, see pages 5–7.

A solution is formed when one substance (a solid, liquid, or gas) dissolves in another substance (a solid, liquid, or gas). The substance that dissolves is called the solute. The substance it dissolves in is called the solvent. Water is the most common solvent, but it will not dissolve all substances. Several other factors influence whether or not the solute dissolves. One major factor is the temperature of the solvent. In this project, you will investigate the dissolving rates of sugar at different temperatures.

Research Connections
SOLUTION AND SOLUBILITY; SOLVENT; SUGAR

Materials
ice
water
1 glass, size 10 oz. [0.5 liter] or larger
1 teaspoon
about 1 cup [0.25 liter] of sugar
thermometer (optional)
record sheet

Procedure
1. Put 8 oz. [230 g] of ice water into the glass.
2. Place 1 teaspoon of sugar into the glass and stir. If all the sugar dissolves, add another teaspoon and stir.

Add sugar a teaspoon at a time.

3. Continue to add sugar, 1 teaspoon at a time, until no more sugar will dissolve. Record how many teaspoons of sugar the ice water dissolved.

Add sugar and stir until no more will dissolve.

4. Empty the glass and wash it.
5. Repeat the experiment several times using different temperatures of water (cool, warm, and hot). Use a thermometer to record the water temperatures, if possible.

Drawing Conclusions
What did you discover about the amount of sugar that would dissolve at different temperatures? Was there a pattern as to the amount of sugar dissolved as the water temperatures rose? What do you think would happen if you used very hot water?

EXTENSION

You can expand this project for a science fair by using other solids, such as mints, chocolate drops, or salt as your solute. You might also try other liquids, such as vinegar or a carbonated drink, as your solvent. Remember to select only one variable to experiment with if you are using this for a science fair project. For an explanation of the scientific method you will need to follow, see pages 5–7.

Surface Tension

Surface tension is a force that occurs at the surface of a liquid. The molecules in a liquid are held together by a force. At the surface of a liquid, this force makes the surface act like an elastic film—like a thin, strong "skin." For this reason, the film can support light objects, such as insects that regularly "walk" on water. In this project, you may perform several experiments to demonstrate the effects of surface tension.

Research Connections

LIQUID; MENISCUS; SURFACE TENSION

Experiment 1

Materials

1 eyedropper
water
1 coin

Procedure

1. Use the eyedropper to slowly drop several drops of water onto a coin.
2. Continue to add drops one at a time. Be sure not to touch the coin or the water on it with the dropper.
3. Keep adding drops until a dome of water forms on the surface of the coin. How many drops can you add until the water rolls off?

Add water one drop at a time.

Experiment 2

Materials

water
1 plastic cup
2 paper clips

Procedure

1. Place a nearly full cup of water on a flat surface. Make sure the surface is stable and does not shake.
2. Bend a paper clip at a right angle and use it carefully to lower another paper clip onto the surface of the water.

Lower a paper clip into the water.

3. If it does not float, keep trying. Try not to upset the water's surface.

Drawing Conclusions

What did each of the experiments show about surface tension? Using the information provided in the introduction, can you explain why the experiments worked?

E X T E N S I O N

To observe how to break surface tension, add one drop of dishwashing liquid to the water dome in Experiment 1 or to the glass with the floating paper clip in Experiment 2.

Soil is the granular material that forms the top layer of much of the land on Earth. Soil is composed of ground-up rock, minerals, organic material, water, and air. In this project, you will investigate different soil samples from around your home to determine their composition.

Research Connections

AGRICULTURE; FARMING; HUMUS; ROCK; SOIL

Materials

1 gardening trowel or small shovel
several containers for collecting soil samples
water
1 large jar with a tightly fitting lid
safety goggles

Procedure

1. Collect a small amount of soil from three areas near your home. Choose a variety of areas so that you get different kinds of soil samples. Place each soil sample in its own labeled container.
2. Fill the jar about one-quarter full of one of the soil samples.
3. Add water until the jar is almost full, and put the lid on securely.

4. Shake the jar vigorously. **CAUTION: Wear safety goggles for this step.**
5. Wait for the soil to settle. The different materials your sample contains should settle out in layers.
6. Repeat Steps 2 through 5 with your other soil samples. **CAUTION: Wash your hands thoroughly when you finish handling the soil.**

Wait for the soil to settle in layers.

Drawing Conclusions

Were the layers different depending on where you got your soil? Did one seem more sandy? Did any contain more humus (organic materials)?

EXTENSION

You can expand this project for a science fair by selecting soil samples from an area that has many plants and an area that does not have many plants. Test the soil samples to see what substances are more concentrated in the soil that promotes plant growth compared with the soil from the area that does not. For a long-term test, plant some seeds (such as peas or beans) in each type of soil and see which is best for growing seeds. For an explanation of the scientific method you will need to follow, see pages 5–7.

Collect a selection of soil samples.

Drainage of Soil

Different kinds of soils have different amounts of clay, sand, and silt. Because soils have different compositions, they vary in the amount of moisture they are able to hold. In this project, you will investigate how much water different soil samples can hold.

Research Connections

CLAY; FILTER; HUMUS; SAND; SEPARATION; SILT; SOIL

Materials

1 gardening trowel or small shovel

3 or more sturdy plastic bags, each large enough to hold 2 to 3 cups [0.5 to 0.75 liter] of soil

sticky labels

1 marking pen

1 magnifying glass (optional)

3 or more clean, empty metal cans with both ends removed (Each can should hold at least two cups [0.5 liter] of liquid.)

masking tape

3 or more pieces of cloth, each large enough to cover the opening of 1 metal can

rubber bands or string

3 or more clean plastic cups or jars, each with a mouth the size of the ends of the metal cans

1 measuring cup

water

recording table

Procedure

1. Use the trowel to collect three or more soil samples from different locations near your home. Choose a variety of areas so that you get different kinds of soil. For example, you might collect soil from your back yard; a garden plot; an area near a river, lake, or stream; a dry area; or a

streambed. Place each soil sample in its own plastic bag. Label each bag with a number that indicates the location from which the sample was collected.

2. Make a table like the one shown below. Fill in the information from the label for each of your soil samples.

Sample/ Location	Color	Texture	Wet/Dry	Water in soil
1–Back yard	Light brown	Sandy	Dry	50 ml
2				
3				

3. Examine each soil sample carefully, noting its color, texture (whether it seems sandy, silty, or like clay), wetness, or dryness. Look for bits of rock in the soil. Identify decaying leaves and other organic (carbon-containing) matter. You may wish to use a magnifying glass. **CAUTION: Wash your hands thoroughly when you finish handling the soil.** Record your observations in your table.

Put the soil samples in numbered bags.

4. Set up three or more devices like the one shown in the diagram below. First, cover any rough edges of your metal cans with masking tape to prevent injury. **CAUTION: Be careful when handling the sharp edges of the cans.** Then, put a piece of cloth over one of the open ends of each metal can and secure the cloth with a rubber band or piece of string. Place each metal can over the mouth of one of the plastic cups or jars with the cloth side down. Make sure the metal can rests securely on or inside the rim of the jar. Label each plastic cup or jar with the identifying number of one of the soil samples.

5. Measure one cup [0.25 liter] of a soil sample and place it in the appropriate metal can. Add one cup [0.25 liter] of water to the soil.

Pour water through the soil sample.

6. Repeat Step 5 for your other soil samples.

7. After ten minutes, check to see if water has stopped filtering out of your soil samples. When the samples stop dripping, carefully measure the amount of water collected in each plastic cup or jar by pouring the filtered water back into the measuring cup. Note the amount of water collected from each sample. To fill in the last column of your table, subtract the amount of water collected from one cup. This is the amount of water the soil sample holds.

Drawing Conclusions

Which soil sample held the most water? Which soil sample held the least water? Look at your observation notes. Why do you think each of the samples held water differently?

Alternate Procedure

An alternate way to investigate the drainage of soil is to collect samples as before but use a different filter design. Use scissors to cut a 2-liter bottle in two, cutting about one third of the way down from the top (see the diagram). **CAUTION: Handle the scissors very carefully or have an adult help you.** Cover the mouth of the bottle with a piece of cloth held in place with rubber bands. Invert this piece of the bottle—the "funnel"—in the top of the other piece of the bottle. Put a soil sample in the "funnel." Pour in a cup [0.25 liter] of water and let it drain through the soil. Measure the amount of water that has filtered through. Record your results on the chart.

An alternate soil filter design

E X T E N S I O N

You can expand this project for a science fair by selecting soil samples from places that support natural vegetation. Select areas that have different kinds or amounts of natural vegetation. How does the amount of water that a soil type can hold affect the type or amount of vegetation that grows in that soil? Also, does the type or amount of vegetation affect the amount of water that the soil can hold? For an explanation of the scientific method you will need to follow, see pages 5–7.

Meteorologists (scientists who study weather) have found that by measuring changes in air pressure, they can forecast changes in weather. An instrument used to measure air pressure is called a barometer. There are two basic types. A mercury barometer measures atmospheric pressure with a column of mercury that rises and falls as pressure changes. An aneroid barometer uses no liquid. Instead, an aneroid barometer measures how much the walls of a sealed container respond to changes of atmospheric pressure. In this project, you will assemble your own aneroid barometer.

Research Connections

AIR; ATMOSPHERE; BAROMETER; METEOROLOGY; PRESSURE; WEATHER

Materials

scissors
1 large balloon
2 small glass jars of equal size
rubber bands
1 drinking straw or coffee stirrer
glue
1 craft stick or tongue depressor
1 thin marking pen

Procedure

1. Use the scissors to cut the end off the balloon.
2. Stretch the balloon over the top of one jar. Be sure it is tight. Fasten it in place with a rubber band. (Use more than one rubber band if necessary.)
3. Cut one end from the straw or coffee stirrer at an angle to make a point.
4. Glue the other end of the straw to the center of the balloon. Hold it in place for several minutes to allow the glue to set.

Glue the straw to the balloon.

5. Use a rubber band to attach the craft stick or tongue depressor to the outside of the other jar.

Attach a craft stick.

6. Place the jars close enough so that the pointed end of the straw touches the stick.

Place the jars together.

7. Make a line on the stick where the pointer touches it.
8. To use your barometer, check the pointer several times a day. Make a mark on the stick when the pointer rises or falls. This rising and falling is an indication of rising and falling air pressure.

Drawing Conclusions

When the air pressure increased (the point of the straw went up), did you notice a change in the weather? Leave your barometer set up over several weeks and observe it. Keep a record of the air pressure each day (such as "very high," "high," "normal," "low," or "very low"). Can you make a weather prediction based on the rise and fall of the straw pointer?

E X T E N S I O N

If you have a commercial barometer, compare your readings with it. See if your barometer rises and falls when the commercial one does. Your local newspaper may also have a weather page that states changes in atmospheric pressure. Compare this data with your findings.

Humidity is the amount of water vapor in the air. At any particular temperature, the air can hold only a certain amount of water vapor. When the air at any particular temperature is holding as much water as it can, the air is said to be saturated. The warmer the air, the more water vapor it can hold. That is why warm air sometimes feels so sticky and uncomfortable.

There are two ways to measure humidity. Absolute humidity measures the amount of water vapor in a given amount of air. Relative humidity is the amount of water vapor in the air compared with the amount needed for saturation. Meteorologists (scientists who study weather) measure relative humidity with an instrument called a hygrometer. In this project, you will construct a hygrometer to measure relative humidity.

Research Connections

AIR; HUMIDITY; HYGROMETER; VAPOR; WATER CYCLE; WEATHER

Materials

1 milk carton, preferably the square, waxed cardboard type (quart or half-gallon [1- or 2-liter] size. Or, use a 1-liter plastic bottle.)
scissors
1 shoelace
2 identical outdoor thermometers
string
2 rubber bands
water
1 piece of stiff cardboard
humidity chart

Procedure

1. Carefully cut the top off the milk carton or plastic bottle. **CAUTION: Handle the scissors very carefully or have an adult help you.**

Step 1: Cut the top off the milk carton.

2. Cut both ends off the shoelace. You need a center piece about 5 in. [12.5 cm] long.
3. Slip one end of the shoelace over the bottom bulb of one of the thermometers, and tie it in place with a piece of string.
4. Use the rubber bands to fasten the thermometers to the outside of the carton or bottle.
5. Make a small slit in the milk carton or bottle directly below the thermometer with the shoelace.
6. Feed the free end of the shoelace through the slit, and place water in the milk carton up to the slit. The shoelace should be submerged in water.

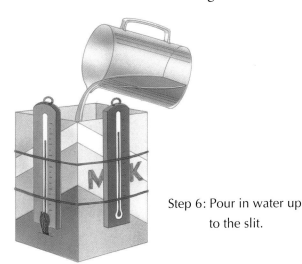

Step 6: Pour in water up to the slit.

The alternate arrangement

7. Place the hygrometer outside where it can remain undisturbed for several days.
8. Before taking readings, use the cardboard to fan your hygrometer. Read both thermometers.
9. Make a table to record each temperature several times a day over several days. Your table should also have a space to record your observations about how the weather feels (cool, warm, sticky, or dry).

10. To calculate the relative humidity, use the chart on this page. First, subtract the wet-bulb reading from the dry-bulb reading. Find the number closest to that reading (in °F or °C) on the column on the top of the chart. Find the closest dry-bulb reading on the column on the left side of the chart. Where the two columns intersect, or meet, on the chart is the percentage of relative humidity. For example, if the dry-bulb temperature is 26°C and the wet-bulb temperature is 17°C, the difference in temperatures is 9°C. This corresponds to a relative humidity of 35 percent.

Drawing Conclusions

Compare your relative humidity readings with your weather observations for that time and day. What observations did you record on days with high relative humidity? What observations did you record on days with low relative humidity? Did the relative humidity vary with the time of day?

EXTENSION

You can expand this project for a science fair by measuring relative humidity over several weeks and noting at the same time the air pressure (by reading a barometer, reading the air pressure in the newspaper, or by calling the weather bureau). What conclusions can you draw? How does relative humidity affect barometric pressure? What is the relationship between relative humidity and barometric pressure? For an explanation of the scientific method you will need to follow, see pages 5–7.

RELATIVE HUMIDITY (PERCENTAGE)																
Difference Between Wet- and Dry-Bulb Readings																
Temperature of Dry-Bulb		1.8	3.6	5.4	7.2	9	10.8	12.6	14.4	16.2	18	21.6	25.2	28.8	32.4	36 °F
(**°F**)	(**°C**)	1	2	3	4	5	6	7	8	9	10	12	14	16	18	20 °C
122	**50**	94	89	84	79	74	70	65	61	57	53	46	40	33	28	22
113	**45**	94	88	83	78	73	68	63	59	55	51	42	35	28	22	16
104	**40**	93	88	82	77	71	65	61	56	52	47	38	31	23	16	10
95	**35**	93	87	80	75	68	62	57	52	47	42	33	24	16	8	
86	**30**	92	86	78	72	65	59	53	47	41	36	26	16	8		
77	**25**	91	84	76	69	61	54	47	41	35	29	17	6			
68	**20**	90	81	73	64	56	47	40	32	26	18	5				
59	**15**	89	79	68	59	49	39	30	21	12	4					
50	**10**	87	75	62	51	38	27	17	5							

The movement of air across the earth's surface is called wind. Wind is caused by cool, heavy air moving in to replace warm, light air as the warm air rises. Warm air rises because it expands as it warms, and so becomes less dense than air at a lower temperature.

A wind vane is an instrument that indicates the direction the wind is coming from. A north wind, for example, blows from the north to the south, whereas a south wind blows from the south to the north. In this project, you will make a wind vane.

Research Connections

AIR; METEOROLOGY; WEATHER; WIND

Materials

glue
1 small strip of paper
1 drinking straw
1 straight pin
1 pencil with eraser
compass (if needed to determine directions)

Procedure

1. Glue the small strip of paper into one end of the straw.
2. Push the pin through the center of the straw and position the straw in the center of the pin. **CAUTION: Handle the sharp pin carefully.**
3. Push the point of the pin into the top of the pencil eraser, making sure that the straw is not touching the eraser.

The completed wind vane

4. Go outdoors and hold your wind vane into the wind. Use a compass, if necessary, to determine the direction from which the wind is blowing.

Drawing Conclusions

Do you think your wind vane would work the same if you glued a piece of paper at both ends of the straw? Why or why not? Why is it useful to know wind directions? Describe some outdoor activities for which you would need to know the wind direction in advance.

Alternate Procedure

To see how warm air rises, cut a spiral pattern out of a round piece of paper or aluminum foil. Place a pencil in the center of the spiral and hold it over a lit light bulb. Observe what happens as heat from the bulb warms the air.

E X T E N S I O N

You can extend this project by marking a square of stiff paper or thin cardboard with the points of the compass (see the diagram). Push the point of the pencil of your wind vane through the center of the square and line it up so that it points north. Then as the vane spins, it will point in the direction the wind comes from.

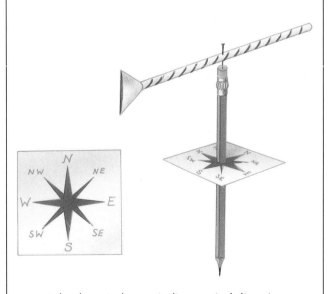

Make the wind vane indicate wind direction.

Meteorologists are scientists who study and predict the weather. They use many instruments to measure the factors (such as precipitation, humidity, temperature, wind speed, and wind direction) that make up the weather. In this project, you will use several instruments you have made in other projects and activities to set up a weather station. By making daily observations at your weather station, you will learn more about weather patterns.

Research Connections

ANEMOMETER; BAROMETER; CLOUD; HYGROMETER; METEOROLOGY; RAIN GAUGE; THERMOMETER; WEATHER; WIND

Materials

compass (optional)
rain gauge (purchased or made)
anemometer (see Activity under ANEMOMETER in Vol. 1 of the *Raintree Steck-Vaughn Illustrated Science Encyclopedia*)
barometer (Project 22)
hygrometer (Project 23)
wind vane (Project 24)
cloud classification chart (see CLOUD in Vol. 5)
outdoor thermometer
recording chart (similar to the one shown)

Procedure

1. Gather as many items as possible from the materials list. If you do not know the compass directions at your location, you will need a compass.

2. Find an open area to set up your weather station. A tall structure such as a clothesline pole would be helpful for mounting your anemometer and wind vane. A safe rooftop could also be used.

3. The thermometer should be set up in a place that is not in direct sunlight at any time of day.

4. Select several times of day to take readings from all of your instruments. Record them on your chart. If any precipitation has gathered in your rain gauge, measure and record it, and empty the gauge. The longer you use your weather station, the better you will become at reading the instruments and observing weather patterns.

Drawing Conclusions

What weather patterns (changes in temperature, precipitation, humidity, cloudiness, and wind speed and direction) did you observe during the time you were keeping records? Did certain cloud types go along with specific weather conditions? Was there a relationship between temperature and cloud density? Between atmospheric pressure and precipitation?

E X T E N S I O N

You can expand this project for a science fair. After recording weather conditions over several weeks and observing patterns in the weather, try to predict weather conditions for the days or weeks to come. Compare your predictions with the actual weather. For an explanation of the scientific method you will need to follow, see pages 5–7.

Date and Time	Precipitation (rain gauge)	Wind Speed (anemometer)	Pressure (barometer)	Humidity (hygrometer)	Wind Direction (wind vane)	Cloud Type	Temperature (thermometer)
7/28 10:00 A.M.	none	slow	high	10%	NE	Cumulus	70°F

The air that surrounds the earth has weight and takes up space. The weight of the air presses against everything around it. On the earth's surface, the air presses equally in all directions. People usually do not feel this air pressure because air pressing on the outside of our bodies is equal to the pressure on the inside of our bodies. In this project, you will set up a test to feel air pressure at work.

Research Connections

AIR; ATMOSPHERE; BAROMETER; PRESSURE

Materials

1 yardstick or meter stick
a table or other flat surface
several pages of newspaper
1 hammer

Procedure

1. Place the stick on the table with several inches [centimeters] sticking out over the edge of the table.

2. Place several layers of newspaper on top of the stick and smooth the paper down to remove as much air as possible from between the paper and the table.

3. Use the hammer to strike the extended piece of stick. Do this with one quick strike. **CAUTION: Handle the hammer carefully to avoid striking yourself or anyone else.**

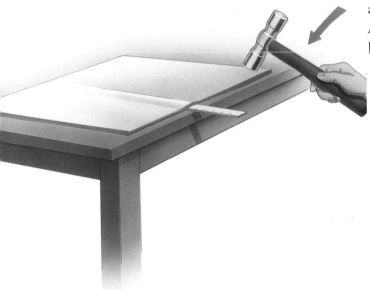

Hit the stick with the hammer.

Drawing Conclusions

What happened to the stick when it was struck? Why did the newspaper not fly up? What was holding it down? Why was it important to smooth down the paper first?

Alternate Procedures

An alternate procedure to demonstrate air pressure is with a gallon [3.7-liter] jar, a gallon [3.7-liter] plastic bag, and a rubber band. Push the bag into the jar and spread it out so that it fits the inside of the jar. Then lift the bag's open edges to surround the neck of the jar and use a rubber band to hold it securely. Reach in the jar and try to pull the bag out.

Fit the bag inside the jar and secure it.

Another method is to fill a glass half full of water. Place a piece of stiff paper or thin cardboard over the top of the glass. **CAUTION: Hold the glass carefully to avoid breaking it.** Hold the paper in place and turn the glass upside down. Take your hand away. Air pressure acting on the paper is strong enough to hold the paper on and the water in the glass.

Carefully take your hand away.

A camera is basically a light-tight box with a window on one side called a lens. The lens allows light reflected from an image to enter the box and fall on a strip of film that is sensitive to light. Because light travels in straight lines, and because the light passes through a small hole when entering a camera, the image on the film is upside-down. In this project, you will make a box camera that shows how a camera works, without actually producing a photograph.

Research Connections
CAMERA; FOCUS; LENS; PHOTOGRAPHY

Materials
1 small cardboard box with a lid (It must be at least 10 in. [25 cm] in length—a shoebox is ideal.)
scissors
1 piece of wax paper
glue or tape
1 straight pin (or other small, sharp object)

Procedure
1. Cut an opening in the center of one end of the box, 2 in. [5 cm] square. **CAUTION: Handle the scissors very carefully or have an adult help you.**
2. Glue or tape the piece of wax paper over the opening.
3. Use the straight pin to make a pinhole in the exact center of the other end of the box. **CAUTION: Handle the straight pin carefully.**
4. With the pinhole facing away from you, point the pinhole toward a well-lit object. (The camera will work best outside.) **CAUTION: Do not point the camera directly toward the sun.** If using your camera indoors, aim the pinhole at a window or other lighted object in an otherwise darkened room. An image of the object should appear upside down on the wax paper.

Drawing Conclusions
Using what you know about light, construct a diagram showing why the image is upside-down. What object might be used in a real camera that allows you to see the image right-side-up? In what ways do a camera and your eyes work alike?

Alternate Procedure
You can use the following alternate procedure to make a camera. Build a camera with a tin can, white tissue paper, a rubber band, tape, and a piece of black construction paper. With a can opener, remove one end of the tin can. Empty the contents and clean the can. Use a hammer and nail or get an adult to help you punch a hole in the other end of the tin can. **CAUTION: Be careful when handling the hammer and the nail and the sharp edges of the can.** Use a rubber band to secure the tissue over the open end of the can. Wrap the black paper around the can. It should extend beyond the tissue end, but be even with the pinhole end of the can to form a long tube. Tape the paper in place. Point the pinhole end at a large, well-lit object. The image should project upside down on the tissue. Try enlarging the hole. What happens to the image?

A camera made using a tin can

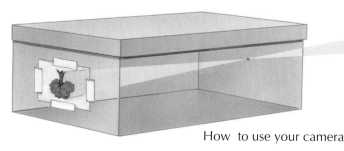

How to use your camera

Making a Compass

A compass is a free-floating magnet, called a needle, that turns freely inside a case. A compass works because the earth is like a giant magnet, with magnetic north and south poles that are located very near the true North and South poles of the earth. A compass works because the north-seeking pole of the compass needle is attracted to the north magnetic pole of the earth. In this project, you will make a compass.

Research Connections

COMPASS; EARTH; MAGNETIC FIELD; MAGNETISM; NAVIGATION

Materials

1 polystyrene foam cup or a piece of cork
scissors
1 bar magnet
1 needle
1 small bowl or flat dish of water

Procedure

1. Cut a small piece of polystyrene foam about 1 in. [2.5 cm] square. **CAUTION: Be careful when handling the scissors.**
2. Use one end of the bar magnet to stroke the needle. Do not rub back and forth, but stroke from the middle of the needle toward the point, ten times.

Use the bar magnet to stroke the needle.

3. Set the needle on the polystyrene foam or cork and float it in the middle of the dish of water.

Float the needle in a dish of water.

4. Be sure the area is clear of any large metal objects that could attract the needle.
5. The point of the needle should point north. If you have a commercial compass, use it to test the accuracy of yours.

Use a compass to check the needle.

Drawing Conclusions

Why was only one end of the magnet used to stroke the needle? Why would other metal objects in the area affect your results?

EXTENSION

Use the bar magnet you used in the above project and tie a string to the center of it until it is balanced and swings horizontally. Tie the other end of the string to a stationary object so that the magnet is swinging freely. Leave the magnet until it stops moving. What do you predict will happen? Why? Use a compass to see if your bar magnet is also pointing north (do not hold the compass close to the magnet).

Electricity: Open and Closed Circuits

A circuit is a path that electricity passes through. The path must be complete, or unbroken, for the electricity to flow. This type of circuit is called a closed circuit. If the path is not complete, electricity does not flow. This type of circuit is called an open circuit. When you turn on a light by flipping a switch, you close the path, which completes the circuit and turns on the light. By turning off a light switch, you make an opening in the circuit and open the path, turning off the light. In this project, you will experiment with materials to make open and closed circuits.

Research Connections
BATTERY; CIRCUIT; CURRENT, ELECTRIC; ELECTRICITY

Materials
1 D-cell battery
2 rubber bands
2 small paper clips
1 flashlight bulb
2 pieces of bell wire (thin) about 6 to 12 in. [15 to 30 cm] long, with the coating stripped from both ends

Procedure
1. Wind the rubber bands tightly around the poles of the battery. Place the paper clips under the rubber bands at each pole of the battery. Bend the clips slightly in the center so that they are touching the poles. This is your battery holder.

The battery holder

2. Using the wires and the flashlight bulb, experiment by touching the wires on the battery's paper clips and on different parts of the bulb in order to complete the circuit and light the bulb. The diagrams show some arrangements you can try.
3. When the circuit is complete, the bulb will light. Draw diagrams of the ways in which you were able to complete the circuit and light the bulb.

When you have several diagrams of complete, closed circuits, compare the drawings and see what they have in common.

Two of the possible circuit arrangements

4. Now try to make a closed circuit with the bulb, battery, and just one of the wires. If you are able to close the circuit and light the bulb, add these arrangements to your diagrams.

Drawing Conclusions
What did your diagrams have in common? Did all closed circuits have a wire at each pole of the battery? Was there a certain spot on the bulb that the wire had to be touching? If so, why do you think this was so? When you connected the materials in such a way that the circuit was open and the bulb would not light, can you explain why the path was incomplete? What do you think would happen if you added more batteries to your circuit?

EXTENSION

You can expand this project for a science fair by using more wires to add extra batteries or extra bulbs to the circuit. What is the effect of adding more bulbs to a circuit with one battery? What is the effect of adding more batteries to a circuit with one bulb? For an explanation of the scientific method you will need to follow, see pages 5–7.

Electricity: Series and Parallel Circuits

There are many types of electric circuits, but they all work in one of two ways. In a series circuit, current flows through all of the components of the circuit together. In a parallel circuit, current flows separately through the components of the circuit. For example, a light, a television set, and a toaster on a parallel circuit each receive current separately. In this project, you will investigate the differences between series and parallel circuits by assembling each.

Research Connections

BATTERY; CIRCUIT; CURRENT, ELECTRIC; ELECTRICITY

Materials

2 rubber bands
1 D-cell battery
2 paper clips
3 or 4 flashlight bulbs with small bulb holders (sockets)
6 or 8 pieces of thin bell wire with the insulation stripped off each end

Procedure

1. Wind the rubber bands tightly around the poles of the battery. Place the paper clips under the rubber bands at each pole of the battery. Bend the clips slightly in the center so that they are touching the poles. This is your battery holder.
2. Assemble your series circuit as shown in the diagram.

A series circuit

3. If the bulbs do not light, check your connecting points and test your battery.

4. Once a closed circuit is obtained (the bulbs will light), unscrew one of the bulbs. What happens?
5. Screw in the bulb again. One at a time, unscrew each of the other two bulbs. What happens? Did you get the same results each time?
6. Reassemble the components as a parallel circuit as shown in the diagram.

A parallel circuit

7. Unscrew the bulbs. Repeat until you have loosened each bulb, one at a time. What happens?

Drawing Conclusions

How were the series and parallel circuits alike? How were they different? Did one type of circuit burn more brightly than the other? If so, why did this happen? Which type of circuit do you think is used in your house? What is your evidence?

E X T E N S I O N

You can expand this project for a science fair by using variables such as more batteries or more bulbs. You can also experiment to see if either type of circuit makes the bulbs burn brighter or makes the battery last longer. For an explanation of the scientific method you will need to follow, see pages 5–7.

Materials that allow electricity to travel through them easily are called conductors. Other materials that do not allow electricity to pass through them are called nonconductors, or insulators. They resist the flow of electricity. In this project, you will experiment with materials to see which are conductors and which are insulators.

Research Connections

CONDUCTION OF ELECTRICITY; CURRENT, ELECTRIC; ELECTRICITY; INSULATION; RESISTANCE, ELECTRICAL; RESISTOR

Materials

1 flashlight bulb with small bulb holder (socket)

1 D-cell battery with a battery holder as described in Project 29

3 pieces of bell wire (thin) about 6 to 12 in. [15 to 30 cm] long, with the coating stripped from both ends of each wire

masking tape

various small items made from different materials, such as a coin, a tack, a paper clip, a marble, a pencil, a rubber band, and a safety pin

Procedure

1. Using the bulb, battery, and wires, assemble a circuit as shown in the diagram. (Tape the wires to the bulb and the battery if you do not have a bulb holder.)

2. Test one item at a time from the list of various small objects. To do this, place both loose ends of the wires on the sides or ends of the object. Make sure the two wire ends do not touch.

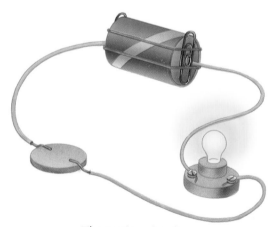

The testing circuit

3. Make a list of which items are conductors (the bulb lights) and which are insulators (the bulb does not light). If none make it light, check the electrical connections and the battery. Test as many different kinds of small items as you can.

Drawing Conclusions

What did all of your conductors have in common? What did all of your insulators have in common? What kind of materials make good conductors?

E X T E N S I O N

You can expand this project for a science fair by making a variable resistor. Use the same circuit assembly used in the first part of this project. Instead of putting various materials between the two loose wire ends, have an adult help you split a pencil lengthwise to expose the lead (graphite). **CAUTION: Be careful when handling the knife to avoid cutting yourself**. Half of the wood of the pencil should be removed so that the lead is exposed but still remains in the groove of the pencil.

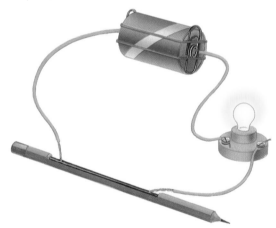

How to set up a variable resistor

Touch the two ends of the wire to the graphite about 1 in. [2.5 cm] apart. Repeat with the wires farther apart and closer together. Does the brightness of the bulb change depending on the distance the wires are from each other on the graphite? Try different materials as resistors. For an explanation of the scientific method you will need to follow, see pages 5–7.

Inertia is the tendency of an object at rest to remain at rest unless acted upon by an outside force. This observation was first formulated as a scientific law by Sir Isaac Newton in 1687. The law of inertia is known as Newton's first law of motion. In this project, you will investigate this law.

Research Connections

INERTIA; MASS; MOMENTUM; MOTION; MOTION, LAWS OF; NEWTON, SIR ISAAC

Materials

1 plastic cup

1 coin

1 paper hoop, large enough to set upright on the rim of the cup

12 small, flat, identical objects (coins, checkers, or coasters)

ruler

Experiment 1

Procedure

1. Balance the paper hoop vertically on the rim of the cup.
2. Set a coin on top of the hoop. (If it bends, make another hoop out of stiffer paper.)

Set a coin on the paper hoop.

3. Quickly yank the paper hoop off the glass. If the coin does not fall into the cup, keep trying.

Experiment 2

Procedure

1. Neatly stack 11 small, flat, identical objects on top of each other on a smooth surface.

2. Set one more of these objects on the table several inches [centimeters] from the stack, and use the ruler to flick it toward the bottom of the stack. If the bottom object does not fly out from under the stack, keep trying.

Aim at the bottom object.

Alternate Procedure

Place a sheet of paper on a table with part of it hanging over the edge (see the diagram). Place a small toy or group of objects on the sheet of paper. (None of the objects should have sharp points or wheels or be able to roll.) Grasp the overhanging edge of the paper and quickly pull it away. The objects should stay on the table.

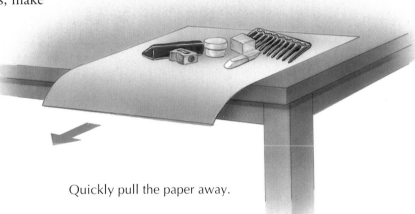

Quickly pull the paper away.

Drawing Conclusions

Can you explain why, or how, each of these experiments is related to Newton's first law of motion?

E X T E N S I O N

To further investigate inertia, see Project 46, Newton's Cradle.

When an electric current travels through a wire, it creates a magnetic field. By coiling a current-carrying wire around a nail or bolt, you can use its magnetic field to make an electromagnet. Electromagnets are convenient because they can be turned off and on by connecting and disconnecting them from a source of electricity. Also, electromagnets can be made very powerful. In this project, you will make an electromagnet.

Research Connections

ELECTROMAGNETISM; MAGNETIC FIELD; MAGNETISM

Materials

3 yards [about 3 meters] of thin, insulated wire with the insulation removed from the ends

1 large nail or bolt

1 battery (A large, 1.5-volt battery with two screw terminals works best, but a D-cell with a battery holder [as described in Project 29] will do.)

paper clips or thumbtacks (to lift with the magnet)

Procedure

1. Wrap the wire tightly around the shaft of the nail or bolt, leaving 4 to 5 in. [10 to 12.5 cm] hanging free at each end. **CAUTION: Be careful when handling the sharp end of the nail (if you use one).**

2. Connect the ends of the wire to the terminals of the battery. (Or connect each wire end to each paper clip if you are using the homemade battery holder.)

3. Place one end of the nail or bolt in a pile of paper clips or tacks and observe what happens (see diagram, right). If the nail or bolt does not lift any paper clips or tacks, check your wire connections or the battery.

4. Detach one end of the wire from the battery and watch what happens.

Drawing Conclusions

What do you think would happen if you coiled more wires around the nail or bolt? What if the coils were closer together? Why do you think these things would happen? What advantages does an electromagnet have over a regular magnet?

E X T E N S I O N

You can expand this project for a science fair by varying the amount of coiled wire or the number of batteries. How does the number of times the wire is wrapped around the nail or bolt affect the strength of the electromagnet? (You can estimate

Try more turns of wire.

the electromagnet's strength by counting how many paper clips or tacks it will pick up.) What effect does increasing the number of batteries

Try more batteries.

have? What is the effect of using a thicker or longer nail or bolt? For an explanation of the scientific method you will need to follow, see pages 5–7.

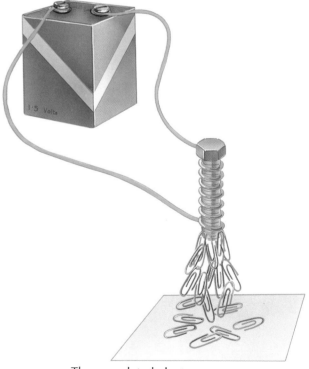

The completed electromagnet

Energy consumption is the term used to describe the amount of energy consumed, or used. A unit called a kilowatt-hour is used to measure electrical energy consumption. One kilowatt-hour is equal to the amount of energy used to light ten 100-watt bulbs for one hour. Power companies compute the electricity bills of their customers in kilowatt-hours. The amount of electricity used is recorded on an electric meter, usually located outside the home. In this project, you will learn how to read an electric meter in order to calculate energy consumption over a period of time.

Research Connections

ELECTRICITY; ENERGY; RESOURCE EXPLOITATION; WATT

Materials

your home's electric meter
record sheet
pocket calculator (optional)

Procedure

1. First, it is important to know how to read the electric meter. It works just like place value in numbers, with the "ones" place on the right, then the "tens," "hundreds," "thousands," and "ten-thousands."

2. Look at the diagram of the clock-type meter. Note that it reads "1 5 6 3 9 kilowatt-hours." (When the arrow is between two numbers, read the smaller one.) The other diagram shows a digital meter, which displays the reading as numbers (digits).

3. Go outside and locate your meter. You may need an adult's help. Record the date and the current kilowatt-hour reading.

4. Repeat Step 3 over several days. Calculate the daily usage with a calculator, by subtracting the previous day's reading from the present day's reading.

5. Do this for one week. Record your results.

6. If you want, make the record for over a month.

Drawing Conclusions

Was there a pattern in the amount of consumption on any particular day of the week (more or less used than usual)? If so, can you think of reasons why? How do you think the readings might change in six months?

A clock-type electric meter

A digital electric meter

EXTENSION

You can expand this project for a science fair. Talk to your family about ways to conserve, or use less, energy. Work with your family to make a plan for cutting down on energy consumption. Will turning off the lights when you leave a room make a difference? Will using less hot water cut down on energy consumption? Again record consumption for several weeks and compare the results with your energy consumption before you adopted your plan. If your plan did not reduce energy consumption, make another plan and try again. For an explanation of the scientific method you will need to follow, see pages 5–7.

Energy is the ability to do work. There are many kinds of energy. If an object is moving, the energy of its movement is called kinetic energy. Another kind of energy is potential energy. Potential energy is stored energy. Energy can be changed from one kind to another. It can also be transferred from one object to another. In this project, you will construct a device to change kinetic energy to potential energy, and then back again to kinetic energy. The device demonstrates the transfer of energy as well.

Research Connections

ENERGY; KINETIC ENERGY; POTENTIAL ENERGY

Materials

2 plastic lids from large coffee cans
1 nail
1 large coffee can
masking tape
1 large rubber band
1 small piece of string
1 large nut or bolt
2 paper clips

Procedure

1. With the nail, carefully make a hole in the center of both plastic lids. (Have an adult help if neces-

sary.) **CAUTION: Be careful when handling the sharp end of the nail.**
2. Have an adult remove the bottom of the can and put tape around the cut edge. **CAUTION: Be careful when handling the cut edge of the can.**
3. Push the rubber band through the hole in one plastic lid and slide a paper clip over it to hold it in place. Put this lid on one end of the can.
4. Reach in the open end of the can and pull the rubber band until tight. Twist the band once.
5. Using the string, tie the nut or bolt onto the center of the rubber band where it is twisted.
6. Pull the other end of the rubber band through the hole in the other plastic lid. Secure it with a paper clip and snap on the lid.

7. Place the can on the floor and roll it along. Observe what happens.

The completed device

Drawing Conclusions

When you rolled the can, you gave it kinetic energy by pushing it. Then energy of motion was transferred within the can. What part of your device do you think took in the energy of the rolling can? What happened when the can stopped? Why?

EXTENSION

You can expand this project for a science fair by trying several can sizes, rubber band sizes, or bolt or nut sizes to see how the results differ. Make an inclined plane (ramp) by resting one end of a board on a small pile of books. Let the can roll down the inclined plane. The steeper you make the inclined plane, the more potential energy you will be giving to the can. Measure how far the can rolls backward and forward, or measure how long it goes on rolling. These measurements indicate the kinetic energy of the can. Try changing the steepness of the inclined plane by using more or fewer books. (Measure its angle with a protractor.) For an explanation of the scientific method you will need to follow, see pages 5–7.

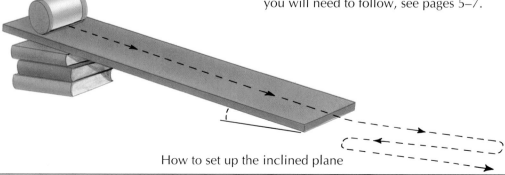

How to set up the inclined plane

Friction is the force that resists the movement of one object over another. It is referred to as a force of resistance. Friction is the force that makes a moving ball stop rolling. In this project, you will observe the force of friction and devise ways to overcome it.

Research Connections

FRICTION; INCLINED PLANE; LUBRICATION

Materials

1 wooden board, about 2 ft. [60 cm] long

1 brick, block, or stack of books (to prop your board on)

1 shoebox

string

a heavy object for moving (book, shoe, or bag of sand)

1 thick rubber band

1 12-in. [30-cm] ruler

sandpaper

glue, masking tape, or stapler

wax paper

Procedure

1. Place one end of the board on the brick, block, or stack of books to form an inclined plane (ramp).
2. Punch two holes, side by side, in one end of the shoebox.
3. Place the string through both holes and tie the ends together, forming a small loop to use to pull the box up the ramp.
4. Place a heavy object (book, shoe, or bag of sand) in the shoebox.
5. Attach a rubber band to the string loop on the outside of the box.
6. Place the shoebox at the bottom of the ramp and pull it up the ramp with the rubber band. Measure how many inches [centimeters] the rubber band stretches as you are pulling the box up the ramp. (It helps to tape the ruler to the side of the ramp.)
7. Now cut pieces of sandpaper to attach (with glue, tape, or staples) to one side of the ramp.
8. Repeat Step 6 and observe the difference in rubber band tension. Again, measure the amount it stretched.
9. Now try it with wax paper. Either remove the sandpaper or attach the wax paper to the other side of the ramp.
10. Repeat Step 6.

Drawing Conclusions

With which arrangement was it easiest to pull the box up the ramp? With which arrangement was it hardest? Why do you think so?

E X T E N S I O N

You can expand this project for a science fair by using different grades of sandpaper (fine or coarse). You may also investigate the effects of reducing friction. To reduce friction, coat the wax paper with cooking oil or glue soft material to the bottom of the shoebox. To observe only the effects of reduced friction, standardize the experimental conditions. Use the same weight and the same slant of ramp each time. For an explanation of the scientific method you will need to follow, see pages 5–7.

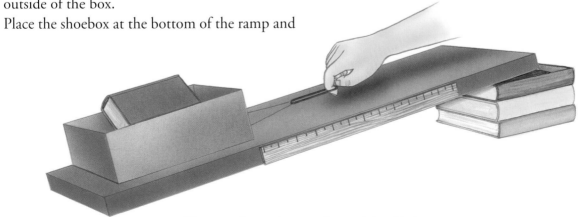

The experimental set-up for studying friction

A galvanometer is an instrument that is used to detect electric current. When an electric current runs through a wire, it sets up a magnetic field. By coiling a wire around a compass and attaching the ends of the wire to a battery, you can observe how the compass needle reacts to the magnetic field produced by the current in the wire.

Research Connections

COMPASS; CURRENT, ELECTRIC; ELECTROMAGNETISM; GALVANOMETER; MAGNETIC FIELD

Materials

2 ft. [60 cm] of insulated wire, with the insulation stripped from each end

1 C- or D-cell battery (Non-alkaline batteries are best for this.)

1 directional compass

tape or small cardboard box (optional)

Procedure

1. Wind the wire around the compass several times, leaving about 4 in. [10 cm] of wire dangling at each end. If the wire will not stay on the compass, tape it in place. Another method is to place the compass in a small box, then wrap the wires around the box.

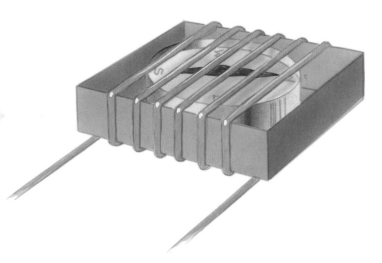

Put a small compass in a box.

2. Hold, or attach with tape, each end of the wire to each pole of the battery. Observe the compass needle.

Using the galvanometer

3. Remove the wire from the positive (top) pole of the battery. Observe the compass needle.

4. Tap the wire on the positive pole of the battery several times. Observe the compass needle.

5. Change over the wires at the battery so that the wire that was formerly connected to the positive pole is now connected to the negative pole. Observe the compass needle.

Drawing Conclusions

What happened to the compass needle when the wires were attached to the battery? Why do you think this happened? Were the results the same when you disconnected the wire from the positive pole? Why or why not? What effect did tapping the positive pole with the wire have? What was the effect of changing over the wires at the battery?

EXTENSION

You can further test the effects of current on your galvanometer by adding more (or higher-voltage) batteries, or by using a longer wire so that more coils can be wrapped around the compass.

Making Gliders

A glider is an aircraft without an engine. There are airplane-type gliders, as well as hang gliders resembling large kites. Each stays in the air by gliding, or riding on warm updrafts of air. In this project, you will construct several paper gliders to see which designs glide the best.

Research Connections

AERODYNAMICS; AERONAUTICS; AIRFOIL; AIRPLANE; FLIGHT; HELICOPTER; WING

Materials

several pieces of paper 8.5 in. by 11 in. [21.5 cm by 28 cm]

scissors

straw

tape

stiff paper

large paper clip

Procedure

Experiment 1

Use the diagrams shown here and on the next page to construct several types of paper gliders. Try each of them to see which flies farther or stays aloft longer. **CAUTION: Be careful when handling the scissors.**

Experiment 2

You can investigate a different glider type with two strips of paper and a straw. Cut one paper strip about 1 in. by 5 in. [2.5 cm by 12.5 cm] and the other about 0.5 in. by 3 in. [1.2 cm by 7.5 cm]. **CAUTION: Be careful when handling the scissors.** Curve each strip into a circle and tape the ends together. Tape one circle to each end of the straw. (The small circle is the front.) Hold your glider by the center of the straw with the circles on top, and throw it. Try changing the size and position of the paper circles.

A glider with circular wings

1. Mark halfway.

2. Fold paper in half.

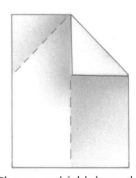

3. Flatten, and fold down the corners.

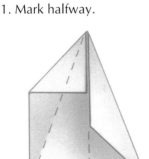

4. Fold each side again.

5. Fold the wings back.

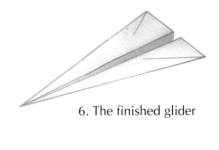

6. The finished glider

Stages in making a dart-shaped glider

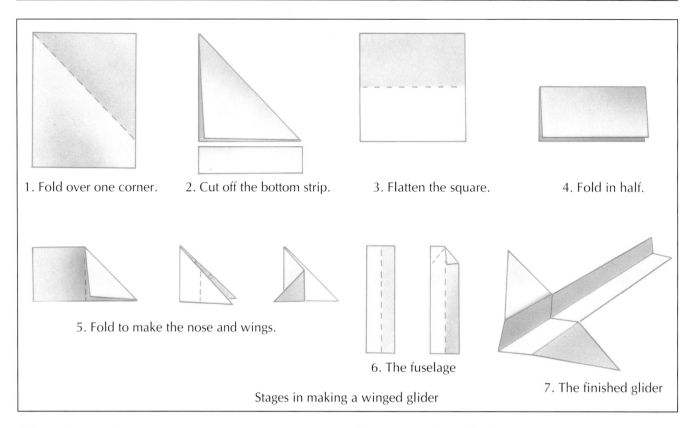

1. Fold over one corner. 2. Cut off the bottom strip. 3. Flatten the square. 4. Fold in half.

5. Fold to make the nose and wings.

6. The fuselage

7. The finished glider

Stages in making a winged glider

Experiment 3

You can also make a helicopter glider. Take a piece of stiff paper about 5 in. by 3 in. [12.5 cm by 7.5 cm] and cut and fold it as shown in the diagram below. Place a large paper clip on the folded part. Throw the helicopter into the air and watch it spin down to the ground. You can alter the angle of the blades and their shape (by cutting off some paper).

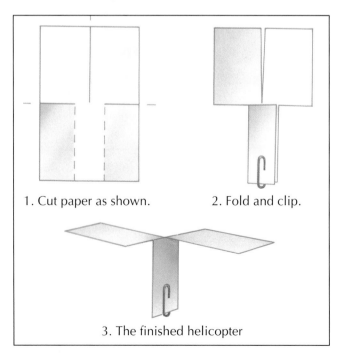

1. Cut paper as shown.   2. Fold and clip.

3. The finished helicopter

Drawing Conclusions

Which glider flew the greatest distance? Which flew the straightest? What modifications can you make to change their flight patterns? Could you make a glider fly away and come back?

EXTENSION

You can expand this project for a science fair by making several similar gliders and then modifying the wings. Try bending the edges of the wings to

How to bend the wings

make the glider climb, turn, or dive. For the helicopter glider, you can investigate how the size (area) of the blades affects the length of time the helicopter stays in the air. For an explanation of the scientific method you will need to follow, see pages 5–7.

Have you ever noticed on a very sunny day that you feel hotter wearing dark-colored clothes than you feel wearing light-colored clothes? If you have ever gone barefoot on a hot summer day, have you noticed that you can easily walk on the lawn, but if you step on blacktop, you get a hot foot? This is because different surfaces absorb the sun's energy differently. In this project, you will explore this phenomenon.

Research Connections
Energy; Heat; Radiation; Weather

Materials
soil
water
2 identical containers (shallow pans work best)
2 thermometers
record sheet

Procedure
1. Select a warm, sunny day to do this project.
2. Place 1 to 2 in. [2.5 to 5 cm] of soil in one container and the same amount of water in the other container.
3. Place a thermometer at an angle in each container. The thermometer bulbs should be submerged in the soil and the water.
4. Before you go outside, record the initial temperature of the soil and the water.
5. Take both containers outside and place them in the sun. They should be set side-by-side, with both thermometers facing the sun.

6. Record the temperature at ten-minute intervals for one hour.
7. Subtract the initial temperature from the final temperature of each container to determine the temperature rise of each. Record your results.
8. Take the containers inside. Record their temperature every minute for five minutes.

Drawing Conclusions
How many degrees different was the temperature in each container when you subtracted the initial temperature from the final temperature? Which substance heated faster, soil or water? Why do you think this is so? How do you think this affects the weather? How did the rate of cooling differ in soil and water? Why did the cooling rates differ?

EXTENSION

You can expand this project for a science fair by comparing sand to soil, dry soil to moist soil, or other materials. Test your other materials as you did in this project. How does each type of material affect the absorption of the sun's energy? For an explanation of the scientific method you will need to follow, see pages 5–7.

Set the containers side-by-side in the sun.

When gases or liquids are heated, they expand. This makes them less dense, so they tend to rise. In this way, warm matter moves from one place to another, spreading heat. This process of heat transfer—in which heat moves from place to place by the motion of warmed matter—is called convection. In this project, you will investigate convection.

Research Connections

CONDUCTION, HEAT; CONVECTION; DENSITY; EXPANSION; FLUID; HEAT; RADIATION

Materials

scissors
1 sheet of paper
1 straight pin
1 pencil with eraser
1 electric lamp with the shade removed
1 large jar or bucket
water
1 small jar (A baby-food jar is ideal.)
food coloring
plastic wrap or aluminum foil
1 strong rubber band
string

Experiment 1

Procedure

1. Cut the sheet of paper into a square and make cuts from each corner almost to the middle, as shown in the diagram. **CAUTION: Be careful when handling the scissors.** Mark the corners as shown.

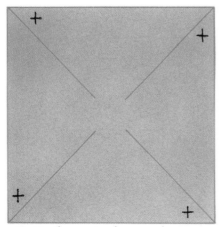

Cut to the center from each corner.

2. Fold down each marked corner, as shown in the diagram.

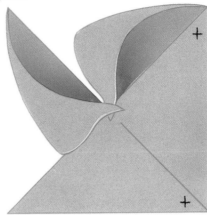

Fold down the marked corners.

3. Place a pin through each corner folded toward the center and through the center of the paper. **CAUTION: Handle the sharp pin carefully.**
4. Push the pin into the eraser of the pencil so that the set-up looks like a pinwheel. Make sure it spins freely.
5. Hold the set-up over the lit bulb. Observe what happens.

Pin the pinwheel to a pencil eraser.

Experiment 2

Procedure

1. Fill the large jar or bucket three-quarters full with cold water.
2. Place several drops of food coloring in the small jar and fill it with hot tap water. It should be a dark color.
3. Cover the top of the small jar with plastic wrap or aluminum foil. Use a rubber band to hold it in place.

4. Tie both ends of the string securely around the top of the small jar to form a long handle.

Use the string to make a handle.

5. Carefully lower the small jar into the large jar or bucket. Use a pencil to make a hole in the plastic wrap or aluminum foil. Observe what happens.

Break the aluminum foil with a pencil.

Drawing Conclusions

In the experiment with the light bulb, explain what caused the pinwheel to move. In the water project, what happened to the colored (hot) water? Why do you think this happened?

Alternate Procedure

To see how warm air rises, cut a spiral pattern out of a round piece of paper or aluminum foil. Place a pencil in the center of the spiral and hold it over a lit light bulb. Observe what happens as the heat from the bulb warms the air.

Place the spiral over a light bulb.

E X T E N S I O N

You can further investigate convection currents. Make a colored ice cube by freezing water containing strong food coloring. Place the colored ice cube in a glass of water and observe how the cold water from the melting ice falls to the bottom of the glass. Explain this result.

Use an ice cube to show convection.

Light Refraction

Light rays travel in straight lines through empty space. But light can bend under certain circumstances. For example, light bends when it passes from one substance to another, such as from air into glass. This bending of light is called refraction. A light ray that is bent when traveling from one substance to another is said to be refracted. In this project, you will investigate the refraction of light.

Research Connections

LENS; LIGHT; MIRAGE; REFRACTION OF LIGHT; SCATTERING

Materials

1 small coin
1 small, shallow bowl (not transparent)
water
1 glass or transparent plastic cup
1 pencil, straw, spoon, or fork
1 square or rectangular glass or plastic container full of water (A small aquarium is ideal.)
1 book (as large as the aquarium base)
1 teaspoon [5 ml] of milk
1 blank sheet of paper
1 flashlight

Experiment 1

Procedure

1. Place a small coin in the bottom of the bowl.
2. Back away from the bowl until the coin is just out of sight.
3. Remain in that position and have someone slowly pour water into the bowl. Observe what happens.

Observe the coin while water is added.

Experiment 2

Procedure

1. Place a pencil, straw, fork, or spoon in a glass or plastic cup three-quarters full of water. Hold the object upright. Observe the glass at eye level.
2. Slowly move the object so that it is at an angle entering the water. Observe the change.

Experiment 3

Procedure

1. Set the square or rectangular container, full of water, on a book.
2. Add one teaspoon [5 ml] of milk to the water.
3. Prop up a piece of paper behind the container to act as a screen.
4. Turn out the lights or darken the room.
5. Shine the flashlight through the water at various angles, aiming the light toward the paper.

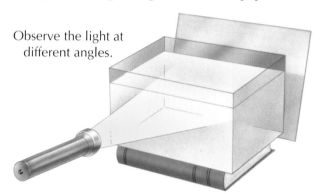

Observe the light at different angles.

Drawing Conclusions

Use what you know about refraction of light to explain why the coin reappeared and why the object held at an angle appeared to bend. Can you explain the behavior of your flashlight beam?

EXTENSION

You can further investigate light refraction by using clear liquids other than water to "bend" a submerged pencil. Liquids to try include cooking oil, glycerine, and rubbing alcohol. **CAUTION: Do not swallow any of these liquids.** Try floating a thick layer of cooking oil on top of some water in a glass, and dip in a pencil. What happens to the appearance of the pencil?

Magnetism is the force that acts between magnets. All magnets are surrounded by a field of force called a magnetic field. Within this field, a magnet can attract (or repel) objects. Although the magnetic field is invisible, it is possible to demonstrate the presence of the field using iron filings. In this project, you will investigate the lines of force within a magnetic field.

Research Connections
FIELD; MAGNETIC FIELD; MAGNETIC POLE; MAGNETISM

Materials
2 bar magnets
iron filings (or a steel wool pad cut into tiny pieces)
zip-up plastic bag

Procedure
1. If the magnets' poles (ends) are not m "north" and "south," place their poles toget they pull together, you have opposite poles (north and south). If they repel (push apart), you have two like poles (two norths or two souths).
2. Place the two magnets on a flat surface with two poles close together, but not touching.
3. Put the iron filings or the steel wool pieces in the zip-up plastic bag. **CAUTION: Do not breathe in the iron filings or the steel wool pieces.**

4. Spread out the iron filings or steel wool pieces in the bag and place the bag directly over the magnets.
5. Observe how the filings line up around the magnets. Make a sketch of the patterns that the filings form.
6. Lift the bag and turn one of the magnets around so that its other pole is now facing the other magnet.
7. Repeat Steps 4 through 5.

Drawing Conclusions
Were you able to tell by the way the filings lined up each time whether you had opposite or like poles facing each other? How were the patterns made by the filings different?

E X T E N S I O N

You can expand this project for a science fair by using several types of magnets (bar, horseshoe, or U-shaped). Find out if the strength of the magnetic field changes as the two poles of a magnet are closer together, as they are in a horseshoe or U-shaped magnet. For an explanation of the scientific method you will need to follow, see pages 5–7.

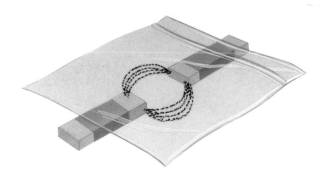

One possible pattern of filings

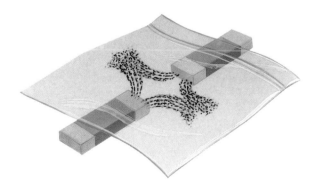

Another possible pattern of filings

Mirrors and Reflections

Mirrors are used to reflect light. A ray of light strikes a mirror and is reflected into our eyes. The rays of light striking the mirror (called incident rays) leave the mirror at the same angle that the reflected rays leave the mirror. In this project, you will experiment with reflections from several mirrors.

Research Connections

LIGHT; MIRROR; REFLECTION OF LIGHT

Materials

3 small, identically sized mirrors (preferably without frames)

several small objects, such as coins

paper clips or pencil

masking tape

Procedure

1. Hold up one mirror vertically on a flat surface and hold a coin, paper clip, or pencil in front of it. Observe the reflected image. Change the position of the object to see if the position of its image in the mirror also changes.

2. Place two mirrors face down, side by side, with a small gap between them. Put masking tape on the backs to join the two mirrors.

3. Stand the mirrors up as shown in the diagram and again place a coin or paper clip in front of them, or hold a pencil vertically in front of them. Observe the image or images.

Observe the images in two mirrors.

Drawing Conclusions

How did the position of the image change in the single mirror when you changed the object's position? How did the number of images viewed in each mirror change when you made a double mirror? How many images do you think you would see if you placed two or three of each object in front of the double mirror? Try it.

EXTENSION

You can expand this project for a science fair by altering the angle between the pair of hinged mirrors. Investigate how the angle between the mirrors affects the number of reflections you can see. Make a note of the angle between the mirrors (using a protractor), and count the number of reflections of an object placed on a line that bisects the angle between the mirrors (see diagram).

Vary the angle between the two mirrors.

Or, try joining three mirrors together to form a triangle (see diagram below). Hypothesize how many times an object's reflection will be multiplied. Then set an object in the center of your triangle of mirrors and check your hypothesis. For an explanation of the scientific method you will need to follow, see pages 5–7.

Using a triangle of mirrors

The light we see is made up of a spectrum of colors. Each color light has a different wavelength. The shortest wavelengths form the blue end of the spectrum. The longest wavelengths form the red end. Between blue and red are the other colors of the spectrum. The primary colors of light are red, blue, and green. The other colors of light are obtained by mixing the primary colors. When we see a mixture of all colors together, we see white. In this project, you will investigate how white or other colors can be created by mixing just a few colors.

Research Connections

COLOR; LIGHT; RAINBOW; SPECTRUM; WAVE

Materials

white poster board (tagboard)
1 pencil
scissors
1 protractor
red, blue, and green poster paint
1 paint brush
masking tape

Procedure

1. Draw or trace a circle on the poster board or tagboard. (A cup or mug rim would be a good size to trace.) Cut out the circle. **CAUTION: Be careful when handling the scissors.**
2. Use a pencil to divide the circle into three equal sections. (If you are using a protractor, each section will have an angle of 120°.)
3. Paint each section, one red, one blue, and one green. Let the paint dry.

Paint the sections red, blue, and green.

4. Make a hole in the center with the pencil point and push the pencil partway through the circle.
5. Tape the pencil in place. Apply the tape to the unpainted side of the circle.
6. Spin the pencil and wheel like a top and observe the colors.

Spin the pencil and observe the colors.

7. Cut two more circles, but this time measure off four sections, each with a 90° angle.
8. Paint one circle with two sections red and two sections green. Paint the other circle with two sections red and two sections blue.

Paint two circles with alternate colors.

9. Repeat Steps 4 through 6 and observe the colors.

Drawing Conclusions

What did you see when you made each circle spin? Did you get the same results each time? Why do you think so?

E X T E N S I O N

You can expand this project for a science fair by investigating what colors are produced when different proportions of primary colors are used. Also investigate how different combinations of spectral colors affect the color you see when the colors are spun. For an explanation of the scientific method you will need to follow, see pages 5–7.

A thermometer is an instrument for measuring temperature. The most common type of thermometer has a liquid—usually mercury or dyed alcohol—in a narrow glass tube connected to a bulb full of the liquid. When the bulb is heated, the liquid expands and travels along the glass tube. The tube has a scale marked out in degrees, and the tip of the liquid in the tube indicates temperature on this scale. In this project, you will use dyed water to demonstrate the principle of the thermometer.

Research Connections

EXPANSION; HEAT; TEMPERATURE; THERMOMETER

Materials

1 hammer

1 large nail

1 small plastic bottle with a screw-on top (A metal top works best.)

1 straw

scissors

modeling clay

cold water containing a few drops of food coloring

1 large, tall bowl or bucket

supply of hot tap water (**CAUTION: Be careful when working with hot water. Have an adult help you.**)

Procedure

1. Use the hammer and the nail to make a hole in the center of the screw-on top. **CAUTION: Be careful when handling the hammer and the nail or have an adult help you.**
2. Push the straw through the hole in the lid. If the hole needs to be larger, carefully push closed scissors into it and turn. **CAUTION: Handle the scissors very carefully or have an adult help you.**
3. Push about three-quarters of the straw inside the top. Use the clay to seal the hole in the lid. (Put the clay on top of the lid.)
4. Half fill the bottle with very cold colored water.
5. Screw the lid on tightly.

6. Set the bottle in the center of the bowl or bucket.
7. Pour very hot tap water into the bowl or bucket to the level of the liquid in the bottle. Observe what happens.

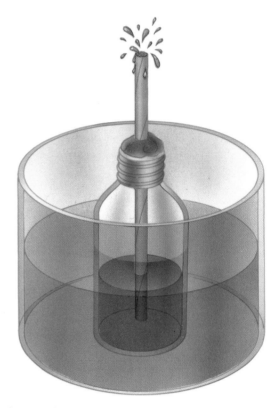

Observe the straw when hot water is poured into the bowl.

8. If the colored water does not rise, place a small piece of clay in the top of the straw and make a small hole in it with a pin.

Drawing Conclusions

Using what you know about heat and expansion, can you explain why the colored water moved up?

E X T E N S I O N

You can investigate this project further by trying other liquids instead of water in your thermometer. Try a "thin" liquid, such as rubbing alcohol, and a "thick" liquid, such as cooking oil. Dye each to make them easier to see. Which of the three liquids, (alcohol, oil, or water) would make the best thermometer? Why?

Sir Isaac Newton was an English mathematician and scientist who lived during the 1600s and 1700s. His many famous discoveries in mathematics, astronomy, mechanics, and optics are some of the most important scientific advances of all time. His three laws of motion, which describe how forces affect the motion of an object, were published in 1687. In this project, you will construct an apparatus called Newton's cradle. The "cradle" demonstrates two of Newton's laws of motion: (1) things at rest tend to stay at rest until acted on by an outside force, and (2) for every action, there is an equal and opposite reaction.

Research Connections

DYNAMICS; INERTIA; MECHANICS; MOMENTUM; MOTION, LAWS OF; NEWTON, SIR ISAAC

Materials

1 ruler
1 pencil or dowel rod
scissors
5 paper clips
5 8-in. [20-cm] pieces of fishing line
5 wooden beads

Procedure

1. Using the ruler to measure, make five marks on the pencil or dowel exactly 1 in. [2.5 cm] apart. The third mark should be in the center of the pencil or dowel.

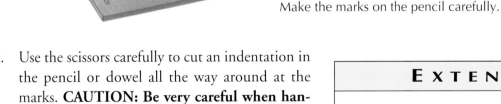

Make the marks on the pencil carefully.

2. Use the scissors carefully to cut an indentation in the pencil or dowel all the way around at the marks. **CAUTION: Be very careful when handling the scissors or have an adult help you.**
3. Tie a paper clip to one end of each piece of fishing line. Be careful to place each clip in exactly the same place on each line.
4. Thread each piece of line through the hole in each bead so that the beads rest on top of the paper clips.

5. Tie each line to the scored marks on your pencil or dowel. The beads must line up exactly and hang evenly.
6. Hold the pencil or the dowel horizontally in one hand.
7. Pull back the first bead on one side and release. Observe what happens.

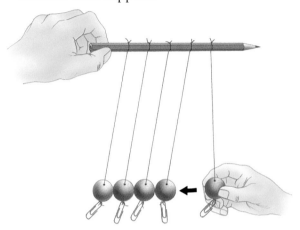

Pull back the first bead and release.

8. Repeat, pulling back two, then three, beads. Again observe what happens.

Drawing Conclusions

Using what you know about Newton's laws of motion, can you explain the results you observed?

EXTENSION

To further investigate this activity, obtain a longer dowel and add more beaded lines to it to see if you obtain the same results. You can also try changing the size of the beads, the length of the string, or the number of beads hanging from each string, and observe the results.

Percussion Instruments

Sound is produced by vibration. All musical instruments have some part that vibrates, or they make air vibrate. There are several basic types of musical instruments, including stringed, brass, woodwind, and percussion. Each basic type of instrument produces sound in a different way. Percussion instruments are struck to produce a sound. The triangle, drums, and cymbals are examples of percussion instruments. In this project, you will make a percussion instrument.

Research Connections

NOISE; RESONANCE; SOUND

Materials

water
8 identical jars, glasses, or bottles
1 spoon

Procedure

1. Pour various amounts of water into your containers. That is, put very little water in the first, a little more in the second one, and so on, until the eighth container is almost full.

2. Set your containers in a straight line, close together, starting with the nearly empty one on the left. Place them in order next to the nearly empty one, from the one containing the smallest amount of water on the left to the one containing the most amount of water on the right.

3. Use the spoon to tap each container lightly. The range in pitch (high sound to low sound) should be music to your ears!

Drawing Conclusions

What caused the difference in pitch when you struck each container? If you used bottles, would blowing into them produce similar pitch variations? Try it. If it works, you will have converted a percussion instrument into a wind instrument.

E X T E N S I O N

You can further investigate sound with your containers by trying to play a simple tune on them. Label your containers 1 through 8. Try to play "Jingle Bells," "Mary Had a Little Lamb," or a tune of your own choice on your containers. As you experiment, write down the number of each container you struck when you feel you have discovered the correct sequence to play your tunes. For example:

$$1 \quad 1 \quad 5 \quad 5 \quad 6 \quad 6 \quad 5$$
$$4 \quad 4 \quad 3 \quad 3 \quad 2 \quad 2 \quad 1$$

Or, you can add different colors of food coloring to each container and write down the tune in terms of these colors.

Arrange the containers in order and tap them with a spoon.

A sound wave is produced when any object vibrates back and forth. The sound travels through the air, or another substance, in the form of sound waves. When the waves reach our ears, they make our eardrums vibrate. From the inner ear, nerve messages travel to the brain, and we hear the sound. In this project, you will investigate how sound waves travel.

Research Connections

EAR; ECHO; SOUND; TELEPHONE; WAVE

Materials

1 spoon
heavy cotton string
1 wire coat hanger
2 polystyrene foam cups
1 small nail
1 hammer
2 small tin cans (or you may use plastic or foam cups)
2 paper clips

Experiment 1

Procedure

1. Tie a spoon in the center of a 36-in. [90-cm] piece of string. Or tie two 18-in. [45-cm] strings to each end of the bottom part of a wire coat hanger.
2. Wrap the free ends of the string several times around your index fingers.
3. Place your index fingers in your ears.
4. Bend over slightly so that your body is not touching the spoon or hanger.
5. Have someone strike the spoon or hanger with another object.
6. Have your partner strike the spoon or hanger several more times, slightly softer or harder. Compare what you hear each time.
7. Carefully make a small hole in the center of the bottom of two polystyrene foam cups.
8. Thread each end of your string through each hole, from the outside in. Tie a knot in the end of the string to keep it from slipping back through the hole, or tape the string in place.
9. Hold one cup to each ear and repeat Steps 4 and 5.

Listen while your partner strikes the spoon.

Listen for a difference when using cups.

Drawing Conclusions

How did the sound produced by the vibrating spoon reach your ears? Did the sound resemble that of any musical instrument you can think of? What effect did adding cups to the end of the string have?

Talking using a string telephone

Experiment 2

Procedure

1. With adult supervision, use the hammer and nail to carefully make a small hole in the bottom center of each tin can. Or use the nail to make a hole in each plastic or foam cup. **CAUTION: Handle the hammer and nail carefully.**

2. Cut a length of string approximately 6 to 8 ft. [2 to 2.5 m] long.

3. Thread one end of the string through each hole from the outside in. Tie a knot in the ends of the string to keep it from slipping back through the holes. If the hole is too big, tie a paper clip onto each end of the string.

4. Hold one can or cup up to your ear and have someone speak softly into the other can or cup. Try this several times with the string taut (stretched tightly) and also held loosely.

5. Then alternate, so that each person has a chance to speak and to listen.

6. Keep trying with longer and longer strings.

7. If you wish, make three or four "telephones," looping each one over in the center of the string to allow for more callers (see diagram, right).

Drawing Conclusions

How did what you heard change when you held the string taut compared with loose? Why do you think this was so? How long could you make the string and still hear the other person? How many lines could you add and still hear?

E X T E N S I O N

You can further investigate sound by using your tin-can or cup telephone to talk around a corner. Loop the string around a metal door handle and pull it tight. The door should be halfway open. Stand on one side of the door and have a partner stand on the opposite side, around the corner of the door opening. The string should touch only the door handle—not the door, door frame, or wall. Make sure the string is tight. See if you can talk around the corner on your telephone. You can also experiment with different types of cups or cans and with different types of string.

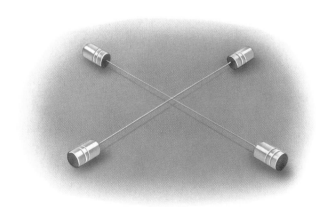

How to make four telephones

Moving air, or wind, has been used as a source of energy for thousands of years. Wind has been used to power sailing ships for centuries. Wind is also used to power windmills. In this project, you will investigate the force of moving air, or wind.

Research Connections

AIR; AIR-CUSHION VEHICLE; SHIPS AND SHIPBUILDING; TURBINE; WIND

Materials

1 small disposable aluminum cake or loaf pan (round, square, or rectangular will work)
1 paper towel or toilet paper tube
1 marker or pen
scissors
masking tape

Procedure

1. Place the pan on a table or other flat surface and set the tube in the center.
2. Use the marker or pen to trace the circular outline of the tube onto the pan center.
3. Cut the circle out of the pan carefully, because the pan will easily tear. **CAUTION: Be careful when handling the scissors and the cut edges of the pan.**
4. Cut off a piece of the tube about 2 in. [5 cm] long.
5. Tape the short piece of tube to the outside bottom of the pan. The tube will stick out like a chimney from the outside bottom of the pan and be flush with the inside. The tape should go onto the tube and then onto the bottom of the pan.
6. Tape all contact surfaces so that there are no air spaces between the pan and the tube.
7. Place the pan rim-side down on a table and blow into the tube. Do not place your mouth directly on the tube, just blow down into it. See the diagram above right. Observe what happens.

Drawing Conclusions

How was air used to do work? How would the results of your investigation have changed if you had used a longer, shorter, wider, or thinner tube? Try it!

Blow into the tube.

EXTENSION

You can further investigate this project by using pans that are larger, smaller, or shaped differently than your first one. See if they differ in motion. Also, you can apply far more power by using a blow dryer instead of your breath. If you hold a blow dryer so that it is blowing straight up, you can "balance" a table-tennis ball on the current of air. This is also putting air to work.

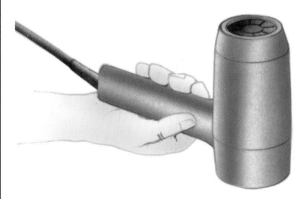

Making a blow dryer do work

A machine is a device that can do work. The work may be lifting an object, crushing it, bending it, or so on. Six different devices are generally recognized as simple, or basic, machines. These are the lever, the pulley, the wheel and axle, the inclined plane, the wedge, and the screw. In this project, you will construct one of these simple machines.

Research Connections
INCLINED PLANE; LEVER; MACHINE, SIMPLE; PULLEY; SCREW; WHEEL

Materials
wire cutters
2 wire coat hangers
2 thread spools
a long piece of strong string
several clothespins
1 small basket or margarine tub

Procedure
1. Cut the bottom part off each of the hangers. **CAUTION: Be careful when handling the wire cutters and the sharp ends of the cut hangers. Have an adult help you.**
2. Bend one side of the hanger down and inward, then thread it through the spool hole.
3. Bend the other side of the hanger in the same way. Bend each end down to secure the spool, as shown in the diagram.

A pulley

4. Do the same with the other hanger and spool. (If you do not want to use wire, put the spools on loops of strong string.)
5. Locate two places to secure your pulleys, such as from one doorknob to another or from your house to your next-door neighbor's house. Ask permission first.
6. Attach the pulleys to each place you selected.
7. Tie a large loop of string around the two spools.
8. Use clothespins to hang small objects from the bottom string. Pull the top string. Observe what happens. You can also make carriers for your "conveyor belt" out of a basket or margarine tub.

Drawing Conclusions
How was your pulley used to do work? When and where might pulleys be used to do work in the workplace? What happens to the direction of the force (push or pull) when you use a pulley?

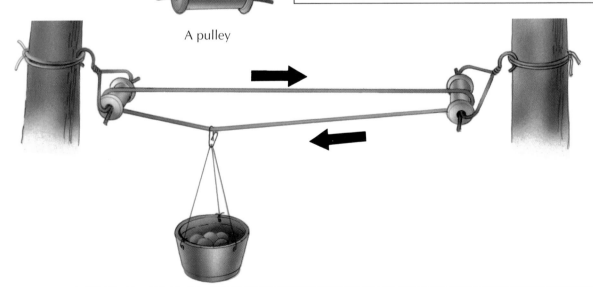

The amount of solar energy reaching the earth is huge, but it is difficult to collect. Not only is much of it absorbed or reflected by the atmosphere, but the heat and light that do reach the earth are not concentrated. In this project, you will construct a device that collects and concentrates solar energy to use for cooking.

Research Connections

ENERGY; FURNACE; SOLAR ENERGY; SUN

Materials

scissors
poster board or oatmeal container
1 shoebox
aluminum foil
masking tape
1 wire coat hanger
1 hot dog

Procedure

1. Make a trough to hold the hot dog while it cooks, either by cutting the oatmeal container in half lengthwise or by using the poster board. **CAUTION: Be careful when handling the scissors.** If you use the poster board, cut a rectangular piece of board 0.5 in. [12 mm] shorter than the length of the box and 3 in. [75 mm] wider than the box's width. (Measure the box opening then subtract 0.5 in. [12 mm] from its length and add 3 in. [75 mm] to its width.)

2. Hold the rectangle on end and curve it to form the letter *C*. Trace the bottom edge of the curved poster board onto another piece (see the diagram).

Trace around the curve.

3. Draw a line from one side to the other of the traced curve, then cut it out.

Make a half circle.

4. Use this as a pattern to trace and cut another. Each of these pieces should resemble a half-circle.

Cut out two pieces.

5. Again hold the rectangle up to form a curve and tape one of the half-circles to each end (see the diagram). This will form a kind of trough.

Make a trough.

6. Cover the trough (made of either the oatmeal container or poster board) completely with aluminum foil, shiny side out. Try not to wrinkle the foil. Secure it in back of the trough with tape.

7. Carefully use a scissor point to make a small hole in the center of each end of the shoebox. **CAUTION: Be careful when handling the scissors.**

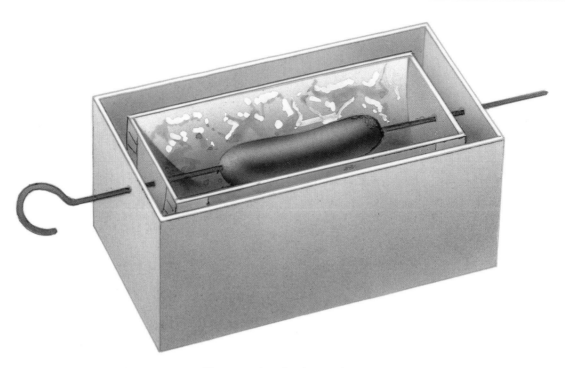

The completed solar cooker

8. Make holes in the center of each end of the aluminum-covered trough.

9. Have an adult straighten out the wire of the coat hanger, leaving the hook at one end.

10. Thread the straight end of the wire through the hole in one end of the shoebox from the outside in. Push it through only a short distance.

11. Set the trough into the box with its opening facing out.

12. Thread the hanger through the hole in this piece.

13. Push a hot dog up the length of the hanger. Keep pushing the hanger until it goes in the holes you placed on the other side of your cooker.

14. Take your cooker outside and set it in a sunny spot. Turn the curved piece up and down until the sun appears to be in focus in the center. Put clear plastic wrap over the cooker to keep out dust and bugs.

15. Check your cooker several times over the next hour to see if your hot dog has cooked. Use the hook on the wire to turn it. **CAUTION: Use an oven mitt to avoid burning your hand on the hot wire.**

Drawing Conclusions

Can you think of anything you could do to increase the efficiency of your cooker? Try designing one of your own.

E X T E N S I O N

You can expand this project for a science fair by spray-painting the foil black or white and investigating how this affects cooking times. You can also test how the angle to the sun affects the cooker. (Use a cooking thermometer to measure the temperature inside the cooker.) You could also try making several cookers to see which shape works best (square, curved, or dish shaped). For an explanation of the scientific method you will need to follow, see pages 5–7.

The most familiar example of the light spectrum is the rainbow. Rainbows are formed when raindrops split up sunlight into the separate colors that make up white light. The colors of the light spectrum are red, orange, yellow, green, blue, indigo, and violet. Raindrops are not the only things that can separate, or disperse, white light to produce a spectrum. A scientific device commonly used to disperse light is a three-sided piece of plastic or glass called a prism. In this project, you will investigate the dispersion of light to produce a spectrum.

Research Connections

COLOR; DISPERSION OF LIGHT; LIGHT; PRISM; RAINBOW; SPECTRUM

Materials

1 small bowl filled with water
1 small mirror (unframed)
1 piece of white paper
1 plastic or glass prism
glass or clear plastic cup three-quarters full of water

Experiment 1

Procedure

1. On a bright sunny day, take the bowl of water and the mirror outdoors.
2. Set the mirror in the water at an angle facing the sun. **CAUTION: Do not stare at the sun's reflection in the mirror.**
3. Hold a piece of white paper so that the reflection from the sun into the mirror shines on the paper. Observe what happens.

Reflect sunlight off the mirror.

Experiment 2

Procedure

1. Take the plastic or glass prism outside on a bright sunny day.
2. Hold the prism and move it around to "catch" the light of the sun.
3. Hold up the sheet of white paper to show the sun's light passing through the prism. Observe what happens.

Vary the angle of the prism.

Experiment 3

Procedure

1. Again outdoors on a bright sunny day, place the glass or clear plastic cup of water on a sheet of white paper.
2. Carefully tilt the glass at an angle until there is a "rainbow" on the sheet of paper.

Drawing Conclusions

Where did the colors on your paper come from? What was the order of the colors that appeared? What other objects can you use to disperse light?

EXTENSION

You can further investigate the visible spectrum with a garden hose on a sunny day. Turn on the faucet and place your thumb over the end of the hose to make a fine spray. Change the direction of your water spray until you can find a rainbow.

Electric charges can be either moving or still. In an electric circuit, the charges move along the wires. However, if an object is rubbed, it sometimes gains an electric charge, but the charges do not move in the object. They are said to be "static" and the object has "static electricity." An object with static electricity acts very much like a magnet. Because it has either gained or lost electrons, an object that has static charge either attracts or repels other objects. In this project, you will investigate the effects of static electricity.

Research Connections

CHARGE; ELECTRICITY; ELECTRON; HUMIDITY

Materials

2 balloons

several of the following: salt, parsley flakes, puffed rice cereal, polystyrene foam broken into tiny pieces

string

Procedure

1. Blow up and tie one balloon.
2. Hold the balloon with one hand and rub it against your hair for about thirty strokes. Rub in only one direction.

Stroke the balloon on your hair.

3. Hold the balloon up to a wall and let go. Observe what happens.
4. Rub the balloon on your hair again and hold it close to a friend's hair. Observe what happens.

5. Sprinkle some salt, parsley flakes, puffed rice cereal, or tiny polystyrene foam pieces on a table.
6. Again stroke your hair with the balloon in one direction about thirty times. Hold it several inches [centimeters] above the small items on the table. Observe what happens.

Hold the balloon over the small pieces.

7. Blow up and tie the other balloon. Tie a piece of string to each balloon.
8. Again stroke your hair with one balloon.
9. Hold both strings attached to the balloons in one hand so that the balloons hang freely. Observe what happens.

Drawing Conclusions

Using the information in the introduction, can you explain which objects lost electrons—the hair or the balloon? Give the reason for your answer. Why did the balloon stick to the wall? Why did it pick up small objects?

E X T E N S I O N

You can investigate static electricity further by selecting one of the above procedures to repeat on a daily basis for several weeks. Check the newspaper or television weather report for the humidity reading in your area. See if there is a correlation between the amount of humidity and how well your balloon responds.

Musical instruments are grouped into four main categories: percussion, woodwind, brass, and stringed. They not only differ in how they are made, but also in how they are played. Percussion instruments are struck, woodwind and brass instruments are blown into, and stringed instruments are played by rubbing, striking, or plucking the strings. In each instrument, sound is produced because some part of it vibrates. The pitch of a tone (whether it is high or low) depends on the speed of the vibration. Fast vibrations produce tones of high pitch, whereas slow vibrations produce tones of low pitch. In this project, you will make stringed and percussion instruments to investigate pitch.

Research Connections

FREQUENCY; HARMONICS; NOISE; RESONANCE; SOUND

Materials

1 shoebox with a lid

scissors

several large rubber bands of different thicknesses and lengths

1 small ruler, 6 in. [15 cm] to 12 in. [30 cm] long

1 empty food can

masking tape

1 balloon

1 pencil with an eraser

Experiment 1

Procedure

1. Cut a circular hole in the center of the shoebox lid about 4 in. [10 cm] in diameter.
2. Place the lid on the box.
3. Stretch several rubber bands around the ends of the shoebox, over the hole.
4. Slide the ruler under the rubber bands and turn it so that it is standing upright on its edge. Hold it if necessary to keep it in an upright position (see diagram at right).
5. Pluck or strum the rubber bands. Move the ruler closer to or farther from the hole in the box. Listen to how the sounds vary.

Experiment 2

Procedure

1. Cut both ends off a can. (Have an adult help you.) Cover the rough edges with masking tape. **CAUTION: Be careful when handling the sharp edges of the can.**
2. Cut the end off a balloon so that you have a large piece of rubber. **CAUTION: Be very careful when handling the scissors or have an adult help you.**
3. Stretch the balloon over one end of the can and secure it with a rubber band.
4. Tap the end of your "drum" with the eraser end of a pencil. Tighten or loosen the rubber band to change the tension of the balloon and tap it again.

Drawing Conclusions

Did you hear a different pitch (highness or lowness of tone) as you plucked the rubber bands in Experiment 1? How did the pitch change when you moved the ruler? How did the tension of the balloon stretched across the can affect the pitch of your "drum" in Experiment 2?

E X T E N S I O N

You can further investigate varying pitch with a straw. Practice blowing a column of air across the top of a straw. Hold the bottom end of the straw closed firmly with two fingers of one hand. Blow across the straw as you slowly and firmly slide two fingers of your other hand up the shaft of the straw. Squeeze the straw shut as you do so to shorten the air column.

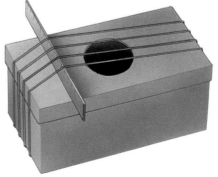

Listen when you strum the rubber bands.

A stroboscope is an instrument used in optics, which is the study of light and vision. A stroboscope can be used to measure the rate at which something moves, or the stroboscope itself can be moved to produce the effects of stopped, slowed, or backward motion. In this project, you will construct a stroboscope to observe its effect on motion.

Research Connections
OPTICS; STROBOSCOPE

Materials
1 saucer or small round plate
1 pencil with an eraser
tagboard or poster board
scissors
1 straight pin
electric fan or other turning object

Procedure
1. Use the saucer or plate to trace a circle on the tagboard or poster board and cut it out. **CAUTION: Be careful when handling the scissors.**

Draw around the saucer.

2. Draw a line straight through the center of the circle. Draw another line at a 90° angle to the first.
3. Draw two more lines halfway between the first two. This will divide the circle into eight equal segments.

Divide the circle into eight segments.

4. Cut a notch 1/4 in. [6 mm] wide by 1 in. [25 mm] deep on each line at the edge of your circle, as shown in the diagram.

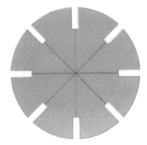

Cut a notch on each line.

5. Push a straight pin through the center of the circle and attach it to the side of the eraser of a pencil. **CAUTION: Be careful when handling the straight pin.**
6. Hold your stroboscope up to one eye so that you can see through one of the notches. Look at a turning object (an electric fan is ideal) and spin your stroboscope. Then spin it again, faster or slower than the first time. Observe what happens.
7. Look through your stroboscope at the wheels on a moving bicycle or automobile.

How to spin the stroboscope

Drawing Conclusions
Describe what you saw. How did the rotating object look when you spun your stroboscope faster or slower? Can you think of reasons to explain what you observed?

E X T E N S I O N

You can investigate stroboscopes further by making others with different-sized circles and notches. You can also make more or fewer notches to see how the viewed moving object changes.

All materials are either electrical conductors (materials that let electricity flow through them) or nonconductors (materials that do not let electricity flow through them). However, if the electric force is strong enough, even nonconductors can be made to carry an electric current. When nonconductors are rubbed together, static electricity can be created. Nonconductors may become either positively or negatively charged when they are rubbed, and this causes behaviors that resemble magnetic attraction or repulsion. In this project, you will make a device called an electroscope, which can detect the presence of an electric charge.

Research Connections
CHARGE; ELECTRICITY; ELECTROSCOPE; INSULATION

Materials
1 10-in. [25-cm] piece of stripped copper wire (with all the plastic covering removed)
1 large wide-mouth jar
1 plastic lid (from another container) slightly larger than the jar opening
scissors
1 small piece of aluminum foil
1 plastic comb

Procedure
1. Bend the copper wire in half, leaving a small loop at the bend.
2. Using the scissors, carefully make a hole in the center of the plastic lid. Push the two ends of the copper wire through the hole up to the loop. **CAUTION: Be very careful when handling the scissors or have an adult help you.**
3. Take the two pieces of wire that are below the plastic lid and twist them together until you have about 0.5 in. [12 mm] left where the ends meet.
4. Pull the two ends apart to form a V.
5. Cut two strips measuring 0.5 in. [12 mm] by 1.5 in. [40 mm] from the aluminum foil.
6. Smooth out the foil and place one strip on each of the copper wire ends by pushing the wire through the top of the strip.

7. Place the plastic lid on the jar with the foil strips and twisted wire inside. You are now ready to test for static electricity.
8. Use the plastic comb to stroke your hair about thirty times. (Stroke in one direction only.)
9. Touch your comb to the copper loop on top of the jar and observe the foil strips.

How to use the electroscope

Drawing Conclusions
Using what you learned in the introduction about static electricity, can you explain why the foil strips behaved as they did? Were they attracted to each other or did they repel each other? Give reasons for your answer.

E X T E N S I O N

You can use your electroscope to test other nonconducting materials for static electricity, such as a balloon rubbed on your arm or a plastic pen rubbed with a piece of fur or woolen cloth.

A vacuum is a space that contains no matter. There is no such thing as a complete vacuum on the earth, however, because scientists have not yet developed a way to remove all the air molecules from a space. The easiest way to produce a near vacuum is to remove the air from inside a strong container. If the container is not strong, it will collapse from the air pressure outside the container. In this project, you will investigate this concept.

Research Connections

CONDENSATION; EXPANSION; PRESSURE; VACUUM

Materials

1 2-quart [2-liter] plastic bottle
water

1. Pour hot water into a 2-qt. [2-liter] plastic bottle. **CAUTION: Use water that is very hot but not boiling. Take care to avoid burning yourself with the water.**
2. Let it stand for two minutes. Leave the cap off the bottle.
3. Pour out the water and screw the cap on tightly.
4. Observe what happens to the bottle.

Drawing Conclusions

When you poured the hot water out of the bottle and then capped the bottle, you trapped air inside. Was this air warm or cool compared with the air outside the bottle? Give the reason for your answer. Did the temperature of the trapped air change over time? That is, did the trapped air get warmer or cooler? How does this explain what happened to the plastic bottle in Step 4?

Alternate Procedure

An alternate procedure is to use an empty aluminum can with a pop-top tab, such as a soft drink can. **CAUTION: This experiment should be done only with adult supervision.** Place several drops of water in the can. Place the can on a stove burner or hot plate on a low setting. **CAUTION: Be very careful not to burn yourself.** As the water inside the can is heated, you will see steam rise and escape from the can. Use a pot holder to carefully remove the can from the heat. Immediately invert the can in a bowl of cold water. Observe what happens.

Leave the hot water in the bottle for two minutes.

Water weighs about 62.4 lb. per cu. ft. (1 kg per liter). Because water has weight, it can exert pressure. The deeper the water, the more pressure it exerts. This is because deeper water has a greater weight of water above it pushing on it. In this project, you will investigate water pressure at different depths.

Research Connections

HYDRAULICS; PRESSURE; WATER

Experiment 1

Materials

1 plastic or wax milk carton (half-gallon or gallon [1- or 2-liter] size)
1 pencil or other sharp object
masking tape
water
sink or tub

Procedure

1. Carefully make three small holes in the side of the carton, one on top of another, about the same distance apart. **CAUTION: Be careful when making the holes.** One hole should be near the bottom of the carton, one near the middle, and one near the top. Try to make the holes the same size.
2. Cover all three holes with one long strip of masking tape.

Tape over all three holes.

3. Completely fill the carton with water and place it in a sink or tub.
4. Hold the carton steady and quickly pull the tape off all three holes. Observe what happens.

Drawing Conclusions

Describe the flow of the water from each of the three holes. Which stream of water shot out farthest? Which stream stayed closest to the container? Why?

Experiment 2

Materials

2 cartons of different sizes (one much wider than the other)
1 pencil or other sharp object
masking tape
water

Procedure

1. Carefully make a hole in each of the cartons at the same height.
2. Cover both holes with tape.
3. Fill the cartons with water to exactly the same height, such as 3 in. [8 cm] above the hole.
4. Remove both tape strips at the same time.

Drawing Conclusions

How do the streams of water differ? How can you explain your observations?

E X T E N S I O N

You can expand this project for a science fair by investigating how water pressure affects the distance a stream of water travels. Use containers of various sizes, but take care always to make the same size hole in each container and to make each hole the same distance from the bottom of each container. Measure the distance that the stream of water travels. You can also catch the water in a container and measure its volume. How does pressure affect the amount of water collected?

Water Turbine

A turbine is a rotating machine that converts the energy of a moving gas or liquid to work. In water turbines, moving water is used as the driving force to rotate the turbine. In this project, you will build a device to demonstrate this force.

Research Connections

ENERGY; HYDROELECTRIC POWER; TURBINE; WATER

Materials

1 empty, round, lightweight, plastic bottle
scissors
1 pencil
2 pieces of heavy string or cord
kitchen sink

Procedure

1. Carefully cut the top off the bottle. **CAUTION: Be careful when handling the scissors.**

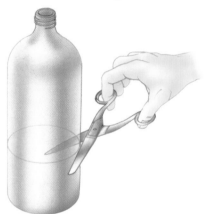

Cut around the bottle.

2. Have an adult help you cut eight evenly spaced small holes (about the diameter of the pencil) close to the bottom of the plastic bottle.
3. Insert the pencil into each of the holes and press it at an angle (see the diagram).

Make holes and press at an angle with a pencil.

4. Cut two small holes near the top of the bottle directly across from each other.
5. Thread one piece of string or cord through each top hole and tie it in a knot on each side, forming a handle.
6. Fasten another string or cord (about 6 in. [15 cm] long) to the center of the first string. Tie the pencil to the top end of the second string.
7. Hold your turbine by the pencil and suspend the bottle under the faucet of your kitchen sink. It should hang freely without touching the sink or the faucet.
8. Turn on the water and observe what happens.

Hold the turbine under a faucet.

Drawing Conclusions

Can you describe how your turbine worked? How would it move if you increased or decreased the water flow? Try it.

Alternate Procedure

An alternate way to demonstrate how water moves a turbine is with a pinwheel. Follow the directions in Project 40, Experiment 1, to make a pinwheel. Use heavy tagboard. Place the pinwheel blades under a running faucet and observe what happens.

An optical illusion is a false impression in the brain of what the eyes are seeing. The best-known optical illusions involve shape and size, but position, color, and movement can also be misleading. Illusions of movement may occur when the eye is misled by a series of events happening one after the other. In this project, you will construct a thaumatrope, a device that is an example of an optical illusion caused by movement.

Research Connections

EYE AND VISION; OPTICAL ILLUSION

Materials

poster board
scissors
1 marking pen
hole punch
2 rubber bands

Procedure

1. Cut a piece of poster board about 2 in. by 3 in. [5 cm by 8 cm]. **CAUTION: Be careful when handling the scissors.**
2. Draw a picture on each side of the poster board, as shown in the diagrams at top right. You may try other pictures, such as a bird and a cage. Be sure both pictures are large and centered.
3. Punch a hole in each side of the card, as shown in the diagram.

4. Thread a rubber band through each hole and knot it by passing the loop on one side of the hole through the loop on the other side.

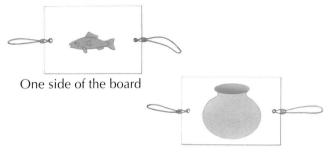

One side of the board

The other side of the board

5. Slip your index fingers through each loop and wind the rubber band as tight as possible (see diagram, below). Release and observe what happens.

Drawing Conclusions

What did you see as the card turned? Why? Try winding the rubber band even tighter. As you release it, also apply more tension by pulling your fingers apart. Does the illusion change when you spin it faster? When you spin it slower? Try it.

E X T E N S I O N

You can further investigate the illusion of movement by referring to Project 55, Stroboscope.

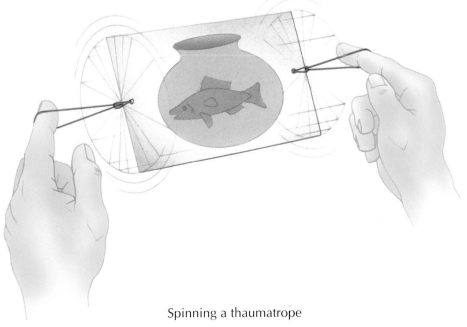

Spinning a thaumatrope

Flower Types

Flowering plants are divided into two separate groups called monocotyledons and dicotyledons. The flowers of each group have a different structure. Monocotyledons have petals in multiples of three, while dicotyledons have petals in multiples of four or five. The leaves of the two types of plants also differ. Monocotyledons tend to have leaves with parallel veins running along the length of the leaf. The leaves of dicotyledons tend to have veins that form a criss-crossed network. In this project, you will investigate the flowers and leaves of each group.

Research Connections

Dicotyledon; Flower; Leaf; Monocotyledon; Petal

Materials

as many different types of flowers as you can find (with a leaf from each plant, if possible)

Procedure

1. Count the petals on each flower. If the total number of petals is three, six, nine, and so on, the plant is a monocotyledon. If the petals total four, eight, twelve, and so on, or five, ten, fifteen, and so on, the plant is a dicotyledon.

2. As you count petals from each flower, separate the flowers into two groups, monocotyledons and dicotyledons. Do you see any other similarities in the flowers from each group?

3. Compare the vein structure of the leaves of monocotyledons and dicotyledons. How do they differ?

Drawing Conclusions

Was it possible to distinguish monocotyledons from dicotyledons just by petal count? How were all mono-cotyledon leaves the same? How were dicotyledon leaves the same? If a flower had a petal number that was a multiple both of three and of four or five, how could you use the leaf to determine what type of flower it was?

E X T E N S I O N

You can further investigate monocotyledons and dicotyledons by observing their seeds. Soak several types of dry seeds (such as popcorn kernels, lima beans, sunflower seeds, or peanuts in their shells) until they are soft. If the seed separates easily into two equal halves, it comes from a dicotyledon. If the seed will not separate, it comes from a monocotyledon.

Count the petals on each flower you collect.

Flower Structure

In all angiosperms (flowering plants), the flower is the structure that is responsible for reproduction. The flower produces seeds that will grow into new plants. Many flowers, such as gladioli and hibiscus, contain both the male and the female parts necessary for reproduction. Other flowers, such as a cattail, contain only the male or female part, and thus must be cross-pollinated (pollinated from another plant) in order for the seeds in the female part to mature. In this project, you will dissect flowers to investigate their structures.

Research Connections

ANGIOSPERM; FLOWER; MONOECIOUS; POLLEN; POLLINATION; SEED

Materials

several different kinds of fresh flowers
flower parts diagram (provided)
magnifying glass
1 straight pin

Procedure

1. Carefully remove the petals from one of your flower samples.
2. Use the diagram to determine whether your flower has male or female parts, or both.
3. If your flower sample has a stamen (male flower part), use the magnifying glass to locate the pollen grains at the top of the stamen (anther).
4. If your flower sample has a pistil (female flower part), carefully slice the base open with the pin. Pull it open. **CAUTION: Handle the pin carefully.**
5. Use the magnifying glass to observe the ovules (immature seeds).
6. Draw a diagram of your flower sample. Compare your drawing with the diagram in this book.
7. Repeat Steps 1 through 6 with each of your flower samples.

Drawing Conclusions

Did any of your flowers have both male and female parts? Did any have only stamens or only pistils? If so, how do you think the pollen from the stamen gets to the pistil? Did you notice that on some flowers, the pollen was located lower on the flower than the top of the pistil? What animals that visit flowers aid pollination by moving the pollen from the stamen to the top of the pistil?

EXTENSION

You can further investigate flower parts by shucking an ear of corn. Originally, the ear was a group of flowers. Each corn kernel is a seed that developed from an individual flower. The corn silk, or hairs, are "tails" that were grown by pollen grains to pollinate the seeds.

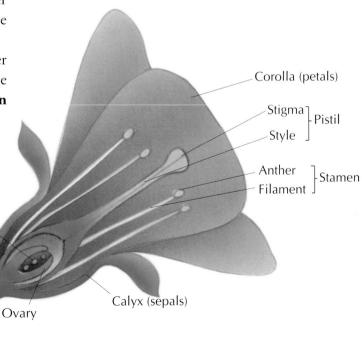

The parts of a flower

Hearing and Smelling

The five human senses are sight, hearing, taste, smell, and touch. These are known as the external senses because they give us information about the outside world. All mammals—including humans—have two ears. A sound takes slightly less time to reach the ear it is closer to than it takes to reach the other ear. In this way, two-eared animals can judge the direction from which a sound is coming. The sense of smell can be overwhelmed or "saturated," so that a smell that was once noticeable can no longer be detected. In the following experiments, you will investigate the senses of hearing and smell.

Research Connections

EAR; NOSE; SENSE; TASTE AND SMELL

Materials

2 spoons
radio
perfume
several film canisters or other small containers that close
a selection of substances that can be smelled (such as cloves, cinnamon, orange peel, a cotton ball with a few drops of perfume, lemon, cola drink, onion)
blindfold

Procedure

Experiment 1

1. Sit down and have somebody stand behind you with two spoons.
2. Ask your partner to click the spoons together as he or she moves closer, or moves farther to one side or the other.
3. Cover one ear and repeat Step 2. See if it as easy to detect how your partner moves with one of your ears covered.

Experiment 2

1. Play the radio at a set volume. Sit about a yard [meter] away, and listen.
2. Put your hands behind your ears to make a "cup." Notice what happens.

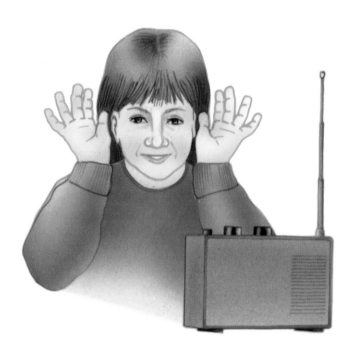

Cup your hands behind your ears.

Listen for the direction of the sound of the spoons clicking.

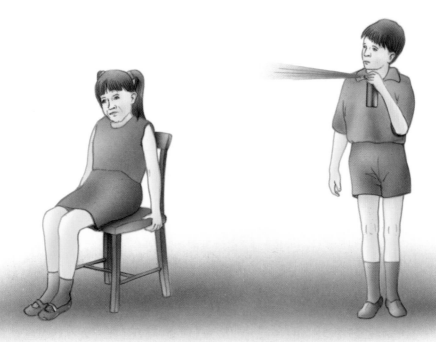

How long does it take to smell the perfume?

Experiment 3

1. Sit on one side of a room while a partner sprays perfume into the air on the other side of the room.
2. Time (or count) how long it takes to smell the perfume.
3. For how long can you still smell the perfume?

Experiment 4

1. Put the substances that smell into the canisters or other containers and close them.
2. Have a partner put on the blindfold. Open the canisters one at a time and ask your partner to guess what the substances are.
3. Switch places. Try to identify the smells while wearing the blindfold.

Drawing Conclusions

Why was it easier to determine where the clicking was coming from using both ears instead of one? What effect did cupping your ears have on your ability to hear the radio? Why could you smell the perfume from across the room? Why do you think you could not smell the perfume after several minutes? Which smells were the most difficult to identify while wearing a blindfold? Can you think of an explanation for this?

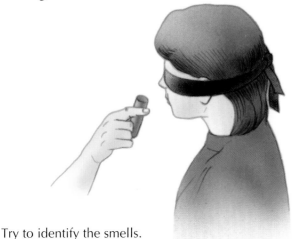

Try to identify the smells.

E X T E N S I O N

You can expand this project for a science fair by investigating how age affects the sense of smell. Try *Experiment 4* with people of different ages. You can also investigate whether smokers or non-smokers have a better sense of smell. For an explanation of the scientific method you will need to follow, see pages 5–7.

The heart and the lungs are two vital organs of the body. The heart, which is part of the circulatory system, is responsible for pumping the blood through this system. When you hear your heart beat, you hear your heart's valves open and close as blood enters and exits them. Lungs are a part of the respiratory system. They are the organ through which oxygen enters the body. They expand to fill with air with the help of a special muscle below them called the diaphragm. In this project, you will make an instrument to listen to your heartbeat, and construct a model of the lungs and diaphragm.

Research Connections

BREATHING; CIRCULATORY SYSTEM; DIAPHRAGM; HEART; LUNG; RESPIRATORY SYSTEM; STETHOSCOPE

Materials

1 funnel or the top cut off a plastic bottle
rubber tubing (about 18 in. [45 cm] long)
masking tape
scissors
1 clear plastic cup
2 flexible drinking straws
2 small balloons
modeling clay
1 large balloon
1 rubber band

Experiment 1

Procedure

1. Cut the top off the bottle to make a funnel.

How to make a funnel

2. Place one end of the rubber tubing over the end of the funnel or the bottle top. (Split the tubing and tape it, if necessary. **CAUTION: Be careful when handling the scissors.**)

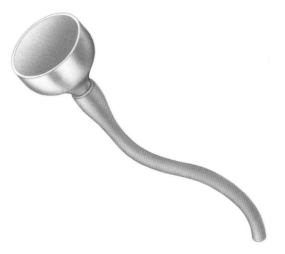

Attach the rubber tubing to the funnel.

3. Place the other end of the tubing to your ear.
4. Set the funnel over your heart. Move it around until you can hear a strong heartbeat.

Listen to your heartbeat.

5. Use your funnel "stethoscope" on other people. If you use it with a variety of age groups, old and young, you should hear a variety of heart rates.

Experiment 2

Procedure

1. Carefully make a hole with the scissors in the bottom center of the clear plastic cup. **CAUTION: Be careful when handling the scissors.**
2. Push the bottom end of a straw into the hole, from the inside of the cup outward.
3. Carefully use the scissors to cut a small vertical slit in the bend of the straw.
4. Cut a piece from the other straw the same length as the section of the first straw above the slit. (See the diagram.)
5. Slip the cut piece into the slit of the first straw. Tape it to make it airtight. Your straws should form a Y.

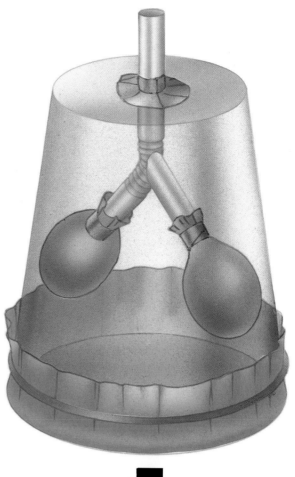

The completed model lung

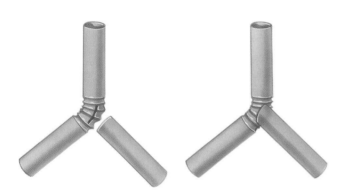

How to make a Y-shaped tube

6. Slip one of the small balloons on each side of the Y, and tape them to make them airtight.
7. Tape the bottom of the Y of the straw to make it airtight.
8. Push the balloons up into the cup until the slit is almost even with the hole in the cup. Use modeling clay around the hole to make it airtight.
9. Cut the end off the large balloon.
10. Stretch the balloon over the opening (top) of the cup. Secure it with a rubber band and pull it tight. This balloon represents your diaphragm.
11. Hold up your model lung with one hand, with the exposed straw on top and the diaphragm on the bottom.
12. Using your thumb and index finger, pinch the diaphragm balloon and pull it down. Observe what happens.

Drawing Conclusions

When you used your stethoscope, did you find that your heart is located where you expected it to be? How did your heart rate differ from those of other people? How is a doctor's stethoscope different from yours? With your lung model, what did you observe when you pulled on the diaphragm? Why do you think this was so?

E X T E N S I O N

You can further investigate heart rate by first listening to your heartbeat when you have been resting for a time. Then, run in place for 1 minute. Listen to your heartbeat again. Continue to listen to your heartbeat as you rest. What happens?

What Foods Do Insects Like?

Different kinds of animals prefer different foods. Some animals are herbivores and eat only plants. Other animals are carnivores and eat only meat. And some animals eat plants and animals; they are called omnivores. Scavengers are animals that eat only once-living material. All of these categories—herbivore, carnivore, omnivore, and scavenger—apply to insects. Some insects eat crops, while others eat weeds, other insects, or dead, decaying materials. In this project, you will investigate the food choices of insects that live near you.

Research Connections

CARNIVORE; FOOD; HERBIVORE; INSECT; OMNIVORE; SCAVENGER

Materials

several paper plates containing a variety of foods, such as:
  apple slices
  banana (peeled)
  bread
  coffee grounds
  flowers
  raw meat (**CAUTION: Always wash your hands carefully after handling raw meat.**)
sugar water
recording sheet

Procedure

1. Select a warm, sunny day to set out the plates in your yard, at school, or in a field. Set the plates about 7 in. [17.5 cm] apart.
2. Place one type of food on each paper plate. If it is a windy day, use rocks to keep the plates from blowing away.
3. Draw a chart to keep a record of your observations.
4. Sit close enough to the plates to see any activity, but not so close as to disturb any insect visitors.
5. Make a note of the types and numbers of insects and other organisms that visit each kind of food over a period of time (for example, one hour or four 15-minute intervals throughout the day).
6. Dispose of the plates and food materials when you are finished.

Drawing Conclusions

What food sample was visited by the most insects? Did any type of insect visit more than one plate? Why do you think that this was so? If you observed at different times, were there any insects that were more numerous at one time of day than another? If so, why do you think that this was so?

EXTENSION

You can expand this project for a science fair by observing over several days at different times to see if the time of day influences which insects arrive to eat. You could make a note of the air temperature to see how that affects insect eating habits. You could also compare how the insects behave when the food is in sunlight with how they behave when the food is in the shade. For an explanation of the scientific method you will need to follow, see pages 5–7.

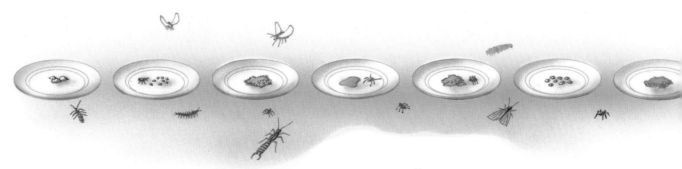

Put the row of plates outdoors on a sunny day.

Raising Mealworms

Mealworms are not actually worms, but rather insects. Like most insects, mealworms go through changes, or stages in development. These changes are called metamorphosis. In complete metamorphosis, an insect goes through the stages of egg (or ovum), larva (or caterpillar, grub, maggot, or worm, depending on the species), pupa (or chrysalis), and adult (or imago). A mealworm is the larval form of a type of beetle. In this project, you will raise mealworms to observe their stages of development.

Research Connections

BEETLE; INSECT; LARVA; METAMORPHOSIS

Materials

oatmeal (not instant oatmeal) or oat-flake cereal

1 large container, such as a gallon [3.7-liter] jar or small aquarium

mealworms (available at most pet stores)

1 apple or potato

Procedure

1. Pour oatmeal or oat-flake cereal into the container to cover the bottom with a layer approximately 2 in. [5 cm] deep.
2. Put your mealworms into this container.
3. Add one slice of apple or potato for moisture. You will need to replace it every few days. No lid is necessary—mealworms will not jump or fly out.
4. Set the container in a warm place, but not in direct sunlight. Changes will occur faster if the container is warm.

A container for mealworms

5. While the mealworms are still in their larval stage, take one out to observe it. Count its body segments. Locate the position of the legs (on which segment of its body). Observe several other mealworms and compare them. Make drawings of them.
6. Check your container every few days to see if any mealworms have changed to their pupa stage. (The pupa is small and whitish, and moves very little.) Make a drawing of a pupa.
7. Keep checking until beetles appear. This is the adult stage. Make a drawing of a beetle. The beetles will lay eggs, which are too small to see. The eggs will hatch into very tiny mealworms. These will then grow and repeat the cycle.

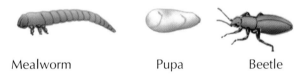

Mealworm   Pupa   Beetle

8. Try placing some mealworms in a small, covered bowl of oatmeal in the refrigerator. Draw diagrams of each stage of development. Compare their rate of change with those kept at room temperature.

Drawing Conclusions

From what you observed, can you explain why mealworms are considered insects, not worms? How were the larvae alike? How were they different? How long did it take your mealworm larvae at room temperature to become beetles? Did the ones in the refrigerator change? Can you explain why or why not?

E X T E N S I O N

You can expand this project for a science fair by conducting an experiment with your larval mealworms. Can a mealworm crawl up an incline (ramp)? How does the steepness of the slope affect the speed of the mealworm? How does light affect the behavior of mealworms? Do mealworms prefer light or dark surfaces? Can mealworms crawl backward? For an explanation of the scientific method you will need to follow, see pages 5–7.

One difference between plants and animals is that while most animals are able to move from one place to another, most plants stay in one place all their lives. Plant movement is usually confined to movement caused by the growth of certain structures, or parts, while the plant itself stays fixed in one place. In this project, you will investigate the growth and structural movement of plants.

Research Connections

HORMONE; MOVEMENT OF PLANTS; PLANT KINGDOM

Materials

1 paper cup full of soil
several seeds common to your area
water
scissors
1 small box, taller than the paper cup
several clear plastic cups
cotton
lima bean seeds
pencils (2 per cup)

Experiment 1

Procedure

1. Plant several seeds in the cup of soil.
2. Keep the soil moist and observe the cup each day until plants grow to about 1 in. [2.5 cm] tall.

Wait until the seedlings are 1 in. [2.5 cm] tall.

3. Cut a hole about the size of a quarter in one side of the box. **CAUTION: Be very careful when handling the scissors or have an adult help you.**
4. Set the cup of plants in a sunny spot near a window and place the box over the cup. The hole should be facing away from the window (see diagram, right). Wait several days and observe what happens.

Experiment 2

Procedure

1. Fill each clear plastic cup with moist cotton.
2. Place a lima bean seed in each cup between the cotton and the cup so that each bean is visible.
3. Turn each cup upside down on top of two pencils, leaving a space between the cup rim and the surface that the pencils are resting on. Keep the cotton moist and observe each day.

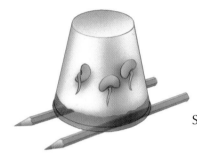

Support the cup on two pencils.

Drawing Conclusions

In Experiment 1, why did the plants grow toward the hole? What would happen if you turned the hole toward the window? Try it. In Experiment 2, what did you learn about the direction in which plants grow?

E X T E N S I O N

SCIENCE FAIR

You can expand this project for a science fair by investigating how the amount of light affects the way plants grow. How does light affect the growth of stems, leaves, and roots? How does the amount of light affect plant movement? For an explanation of the scientific method you will need to follow, see pages 5–7.

Place the box near a window.

Photosynthesis is the process by which green plants make food. It is a complex series of chemical reactions in which plants use energy from the sun as well as water and carbon dioxide. In this project, you will investigate what happens to plants in the absence of sunlight.

Research Connections

CHLOROPHYLL; LEAF; LIGHT; PHOTOSYNTHESIS; PLANT KINGDOM

Materials

several live plants (You may use plants growing in your yard, but ask permission first.)
aluminum foil
colored pencils

Procedure

1. Use aluminum foil to completely cover several leaves on different plants. Make sure that the leaves are completely covered. Do this carefully, so that you do not break the leaf from the plant.

2. Wait several days and unwrap some of the leaves. Observe what has happened to them. Make a colored drawing of the leaves.

3. After several more days, unwrap the remaining leaves. Observe what has happened to them and compare them with the drawing of the leaves from Step 2.

Drawing Conclusions

Compare the color of the leaves you uncovered first with the color of the leaves that were not covered. How did they differ? How did the leaves you unwrapped last compare in color with those you unwrapped first? How did their color compare with that of unwrapped leaves? Why do you think this was so?

EXTENSION

You can expand this project for a science fair by experimenting with different colors of light. Completely cover several plants with "tents" of colored cellophane (such as the cellophane used to wrap Easter baskets). How does the color of light affect plant growth? Make a hypothesis to predict how each color of cellophane might affect the plant. For an explanation of the scientific method you will need to follow, see pages 5–7.

Cover a plant with colored cellophane.

On each plant, cover several leaves with foil.

In addition to light, plants need water to carry out photosynthesis. Since food-making occurs in the leaves, but water is taken in through the roots, plants must have the ability to transport water from the roots to the leaves. In this project, you will investigate how this movement occurs.

Research Connections

LEAF; OSMOSIS; PLANT KINGDOM; ROOT; TRANSPIRATION

Materials

red and blue food coloring
2 glasses or clear plastic cups
water
several stalks of celery with leaves still attached, or several white carnations with long stems
knife

Procedure

1. Place several drops of red food coloring in one glass or cup, and several drops of blue food coloring in the other. Half fill each with water.
2. Carefully cut the very bottom end from each celery stalk or carnation stem. **CAUTION: Be careful when handling the knife.**
3. Place several stalks or stems in each glass or cup.

4. Wait several hours and observe what happens. If no difference is observed, let the glasses sit overnight.
5. Use your fingernail to split the celery stalk or carnation stem to observe the water transport systems. Observe also the leaves of the celery and the petals of the carnation.

Drawing Conclusions

You have learned that food-making is a leaf function and the absorption of water and minerals is a root function. What do you think is a function of the stem? What is your evidence? What would happen if you split a stalk or stem halfway up and placed each side in liquid of a different color? Try it.

EXTENSION

In this project, you observed how a leaf receives water. You can investigate how leaves release water by placing a plastic bag over the leafy branch of a tree or bush. Tie a string or wrap a rubber band around the opening of the bag to seal the bag around the branch. Wait several hours and observe what happens inside the bag.

Place some stalks in the red water and some stalks in the blue water.

Tie a plastic bag over a branch.

Recycling is the process of collecting wastes to obtain materials that can be used again. Recycled wastes provide materials for many new products. Recycling has many advantages. Recycling aluminum, glass, and paper requires much less energy than producing these substances from raw materials. In this project, you will investigate the recycling process by making recycled paper.

Research Connections

ENERGY; NATURAL RESOURCE; NONRENEWABLE RESOURCE; PAPER; RECYCLING; RESOURCE EXPLOITATION; WASTE DISPOSAL

Materials

1 wooden frame (5 in. by 7 in. [13 cm by 18 cm] or 8 in. by 10 in. [20 cm by 25 cm]) (An old picture frame with the glass removed is ideal.)

mesh screen to fit the frame

stapler

paper scraps (various kinds, such as notebook paper, newspaper, construction paper, and tissue)

blender

water

large spoon

newspaper

rolling pin or empty bottle (optional)

Procedure

1. Prepare your screen frame. Staple the screen tightly over the wooden frame. Staple it several times on each side.

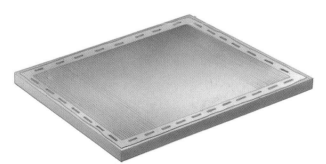

Staple the screen onto the frame.

2. Tear up enough paper scraps into pieces about the size of your fingernail to fill a third of the blender container. Soak the paper scraps in water overnight.

3. Pour the paper and water mixture into the blender. Add more water if necessary to fill two-thirds of the container. Turn the blender on for one minute. If your mixture is not slick and slimy, add more water and blend again.

4. Pour the blended mixture over the screened frame. Use the back of a large spoon to smooth out the mixture to fill the screened area.

5. Lay several layers of newspaper over and under the screened frame. Push down firmly to squeeze out the water. Replace the newspaper with dry layers when necessary. You may wish to use a rolling pin or an empty bottle to apply pressure.

Apply pressure with a bottle.

6. Allow the mixture to dry thoroughly before attempting to remove the last piece of newspaper from the top. If it sticks to your recycled paper, allow more drying time.

Drawing Conclusions

Although you may have thought you wasted a lot of newspaper in the drying process (it can still be recycled), can you understand why recycling paper uses fewer natural resources than making paper from raw materials? What recycled products can you buy to cut down on resource usage? What things can you reuse that would otherwise end up as garbage in a landfill?

EXTENSION

You can further investigate paper-making by varying the amount and colors of construction paper scraps you use. You can make a beautiful piece of artwork by adding leaves, feathers, or scraps of yarn to your paper "slurry" before you press it into the frame.

A reflex is an automatic action in response to a stimulus. Doctors often test a person's reflexes to make sure his or her nervous system is working properly. In this project, you will conduct a test for reflex speed, or reaction time.

Research Connections
NERVE CELL; NERVOUS SYSTEM; REFLEX

Materials
1 ruler (marked in centimeters)
record sheet
several test subjects

Procedure
1. Grip the end of the ruler with your thumb and index finger and hold it vertically.
2. Have a partner hold his or her hand directly below the ruler. Release the ruler. Have your partner catch it with his or her thumb and index finger as soon as you release the ruler. (Have your partner try catching the ruler several times before testing.)

How to hold the ruler

3. Record the centimeter mark your partner is touching when the ruler is caught. Use the following chart to convert the distance to a time in seconds. For the best results, do several tests with the same partner and calculate the average reflex time.

Distance in cm to nearest cm	Reflex time in seconds
1	0.045
2	0.064
3	0.078
4	0.090
5	0.101
6	0.110
7	0.119
8	0.127
9	0.135
10	0.142

4. Change places and have your partner test you. Record the results.
5. Test several other people and record their average reaction times.

Drawing Conclusions
Which of you had the fastest reflex time? Who had the slowest? How do you think the time would differ if you used your nondominant hand? (That is, if you are right-handed, how do you think your left-handed response would differ?) Try it.

E X T E N S I O N

You can expand this project for a science fair by investigating if age, gender (male or female), or changing hands affects reflex time. For an explanation of the scientific method you will need to follow, see pages 5–7.

The cotyledon is the part of a plant seed that processes stored food from storage tissues in the seed. The cotyledon digests the food and passes it on to the embryo (the undeveloped plant within the seed). Although it is often called a seed leaf, a cotyledon is not a leaf at all. A cotyledon resembles a leaf because, in many plants, it forms at the top of the stem where leaves develop. Once true leaves do develop and produce food, the cotyledon dies and falls off. The seeds of all flowering plants have one or two cotyledons. In this project, you will germinate seeds to observe their cotyledons.

Research Connections

COTYLEDON; DICOTYLEDON; GERMINATION; MONOCOTYLEDON; PLANT KINGDOM; SEED

Materials

several small paper cups of soil
several easy-to-grow seeds (such as lima beans, corn, peanuts, sunflower seeds)
1 marking pen
water

Procedure

1. Place several seeds of one type in each cup. Label each cup with the name of the seed it contains.
2. Water the cups of seeds and place them in a sunny spot outdoors or on a window ledge.
3. Observe the cups daily, and water them when the soil is dry.
4. As the plants sprout, or break through the soil, notice the thick structure or structures that emerge before the true leaves. Leaves should develop above these structures, which are the cotyledons, or seed leaves.

Drawing Conclusions

Which plants had one seed leaf and were therefore monocotyledons? Which plants had two seed leaves and were therefore dicotyledons? Why do you think there was any difference?

E X T E N S I O N

You can further investigate seed leaves by researching which plants have cotyledons that stay underground or that have varying numbers of seed leaves. Locate seeds for these plants. Grow them and observe what happens when they sprout.

Count the number of seed leaves on each young plant.

What Animals Does Soil Contain?

When you think of an animal's habitat, places like a forest, ocean, or desert probably come to mind. But habitats are anywhere that animals live, including your own back yard. In this project, you will investigate a sample of soil to see what animals it contains.

Research Connections

COMMUNAL ANIMALS; ECOSYSTEM; HABITAT; SOIL

Materials

magnifying glass
shovel, garden trowel, or old spoon
strainer
funnel
large jar
water
angle-neck lamp
paper towel or newspaper

Procedure

GET AN ADULT'S PERMISSION TO DIG BEFORE YOU BEGIN THIS PROJECT.

1. Kneel on the ground and use your magnifying glass to look at the surface of the ground. Look for insects or other small animals that are in the grass or top layer of soil.
2. Dig up enough soil to fill the strainer half-full. Place the strainer in the funnel, and place the funnel in the neck of the jar. **CAUTION: If your jar is glass, be careful to avoid breaking it.** Moisten the soil with a few drops of water.
3. Take the jar indoors and set it on a table or counter.
4. Place the lamp over the strainer, but not touching it, and turn on the lamp (see diagram, right).
5. Wait half an hour. If no organisms have collected in the jar, wait another half hour.
6. Turn off the lamp and check the jar. Remove the funnel and strainer, and pour any organisms collected in the jar onto a paper towel or newspaper to get a better look with your magnifying glass.
7. Turn the strainer of soil onto another paper towel or newspaper, and look through it for any organisms that are too large to crawl through the holes in the strainer.

8. Make a drawing of the organisms, and keep a record of how many there are of each kind.
9. Repeat with as many soil samples as you wish. Either dig deeper into the hole you dug before, or dig in another place.
10. Return all organisms, soil, and grass to the place where you found them. **CAUTION: Wash your hands thoroughly after this experiment.**

Drawing Conclusions

You should have observed a variety of organisms in all the soil samples. Why do you think they worked their way down away from the lamp and into the jar? Did you observe different organisms as you dug deeper? Did you find different organisms in different places? Why do you think this was so? What necessities (food, water, and shelter) do you think the soil provided for each organism you found?

E X T E N S I O N

You can expand this project for a science fair by first researching which organisms live in different layers of soil. Then hypothesize what you will find before you begin your investigation. You could investigate whether moisture or the type of vegetation affects the number of organisms found in a particular kind of soil. For an explanation of the scientific method you will need to follow, see pages 5–7.

Set the soil sample under a lamp.

Taste and Touch

The body's external senses, which provide information about the outside world, include taste, touch, smell, sight, and hearing. These senses are triggered when things in our environment stimulate special nerve cells called receptors that are located in sense organs. The receptors send nerve impulses along sensory nerves to the brain. The brain interprets the nerve impulses. In the following experiments, you will see that receptors can sometimes be fooled into giving you false information.

Research Connections

BRAIN; EAR; EYE AND VISION; NOSE; SENSE; TASTE AND SMELL; TOUCH

Materials

blindfold
1 plate
small cubes of raw fruit and vegetables (such as apple, carrot, cucumber, peach, pear, potato)
pencil and paper
3 bowls of water (1 cold, 1 lukewarm, and 1 hot [tap water, not *too* hot])
record sheet

Procedure

Experiment 1

1. Ask a partner to put on the blindfold and hold his or her nose.
2. Place one fruit or vegetable cube on your partner's tongue and ask him or her to identify it. **CAUTION: Be sure your hands are clean.**
3. Write down your partner's reply and what the cube really is.
4. Repeat with other food cubes.

How to do the taste test

Experiment 2

1. Set the three bowls of water in a row on a table or counter.
2. Put one hand in the cold water and the other hand in the hot water. Hold them there for two minutes.

One hand in cold water, one in hot

3. Now place both hands at the same time in the lukewarm water.

Both hands in warm water

Drawing Conclusions

When you and your partner tasted each food, were you able to identify all of them correctly? Why do you think this was so? Do you think the results would be the same if you did not hold your nose? Try it. How did the lukewarm water feel to each of your hands? Why do you think this was so?

EXTENSION

You can expand this project for a science fair by investigating how age affects the sense of taste. Try Experiment 1 with people of different ages. You can also investigate whether smokers or non-smokers have a better sense of taste. For an explanation of the scientific method you will need to follow, see pages 5–7.

The earthworm has a primitive brain that allows it to respond to heat, light, and touch, without the use of sense organs. Each segment of the earthworm's body, except the first and last, has four pairs of stiff bristles. The earthworm uses its bristles for movement. In this project, you will investigate earthworms, observe their bristles, and experiment to observe how earthworms respond to heat, light, and touch.

Research Connections

COMPOST; EARTHWORM; FERTILIZER; SOIL; WORM

Materials

earthworms, bought at a bait shop or found in the yard
magnifying glass
paper towels
water
shoebox lid (optional)
books (optional)
soil
container
lamp (preferably an angle-neck lamp)

Procedure

1. Use the magnifying glass to observe an earthworm up close. How can you tell the back end from the front? Does it have eyes? Can you see the bristles? Watch the worm move. Can it go forward and backward?

2. Place the earthworm on a slanted surface, such as the lid of a shoebox propped up by books. Can it crawl up? Touch the worm. Does it move faster or slower?

Test a worm's movement on a slope.

3. Wet half a paper towel. Set an earthworm halfway on the wet side and halfway on the dry side. Observe where the earthworm moves. Try this several times. Does the worm seem to prefer one side to the other?

4. Set several earthworms in the center of a container of soil. Place a lamp at one end and turn it on. Observe what happens. Do the worms go toward or away from the light?

Testing worms' reactions to light

5. Pour water into the soil on the side that the worms went to. Observe what happens.

Drawing Conclusions

How did each of the earthworm's features that you observed help the earthworm live in its natural environment (moist soil)?

E X T E N S I O N

You can expand this project for a science fair by investigating the effects of worm casts on plant growth. Worm casts are the small mounds of earth that earthworms leave on the surface of soil. Grow several groups of plants. Use eggshells, coffee grounds, and worm casts as natural fertilizers. Use one type for each group of plants to see which works the best to increase plant growth. For an explanation of the scientific method you will need to follow, see pages 5–7.

ACTIVITIES

Volumes 1 to 22 of the *Raintree Steck-Vaughn Illustrated Science Encyclopedia* contain short projects called activities. In the list below, the name of each activity is followed by the volume and page number where it can be found. For example, **Anther—How to see pollen 2:101** indicates that this activity about pollen can be found on page 101 of volume 2.

INDEX